The 12 Step Journal:

Using the Tools of the Program,

One Day at a Time,

for Recovery and Serenity

The 12 Step Journal:

Using the Tools of the Program, One Day at a Time, For Recovery and Serenity

www.12stepjournals.com

Help us reach others who would benefit from this book by leaving a review on Amazon (if purchased there) or on our website: www.12stepjournals.com

Published by Alver Valley Press

Printed in China

First Edition 2019

ISBN: 978-1-9165059-0-2

God, grant me the serenity
To accept the things I cannot change,
Courage to change the things I can,
And wisdom to know the difference.

Living one day at a time,
Enjoying one moment at a time,
Accepting hardship as the pathway to peace.
Taking, as He did, this sinful world as it is,
Not as I would have it.
Trusting that He will make all things right
if I surrender to His will.
That I may be reasonably happy in this life,
And supremely happy with Him forever in the next.
Amen

Serenity Prayer
Bill P. and Lisa D. *The 12 Step Prayer Book. 2nd ed.* Center City, Minn.: Hazelden, 2004

Welcome

A very warm and heartfelt welcome to my fellow travellers. This journal is for you if you are working a Twelve Step program, whether you're just starting out, or are a seasoned veteran; and whatever your addiction(s) may be. Welcome all.

The Twelve Steps, and the resulting freedom from my addiction, have transformed my life from one of misery, isolation, angst, loneliness and stress, to one of peace, love, honesty, kindness and connection. They have taught me how to be a better person, a person that I actually like and respect.

This journal has been created out of the overwhelmingly striking pattern I've seen in the meetings I attend: Those of us who apply the principles and tools of the twelve step program *consistently, every day,* recover. And we don't just recover, we fly. And those of us who don't make the principles and tools of the program part of our *daily* life, go on struggling. We often get periods of sobriety and fleeting glimpses of serenity, but we remain stuck in our problematic thinking and way of being.

The same pattern can be seen when looking at any one person. When recovery activities are prioritised *each day,* our life simply flows, and we gain distance from our addictions. And when complacency creeps in and we start neglecting our toolkit, things quickly go downhill. I think each of us in recovery has experienced this, I certainly have, countless times.

The Big Book of Alcoholics Anonymous tells us *"It is easy to let up on the spiritual program of action and rest on our laurels. We are headed for trouble if we do, for alcohol is a subtle foe. We are not cured of alcoholism. What we really have is a daily reprieve contingent on the maintenance of our spiritual condition[1]."* We know this applies to all addictions, not just alcoholism.

So daily action is what's needed to maintain our spiritual condition. But so many of us struggle with this. We know what we must do, but can't seem to do it with any consistency. We don't keep the principles of the program front of mind. Life gets in the way. We don't have people to remind us every day of all the tools we have at our disposal.

I worked with several other Twelve Step travellers to develop this journal. It has been created to remind and encourage us to prioritise our recovery activities, and to use our spiritual toolkit consistently, each day, one day at a time. It will help keep us accountable, and help us to see a way forward when our recovery gets off-track. It's been created out of love, and is based around 12 key tools of recovery, which are explained in the following pages.

Our sincere hope is that this book will help you in your recovery from addiction and on your path towards serenity.

We would truly love to hear about your experiences with the journal, your questions, suggestions and comments. All will be gratefully received, read personally by us, and responded to where possible. Get in touch: recovery@12stepjournals.com

The 12 Step Journal Team

---

1. Alcoholics Anonymous. (2001). *Alcoholics Anonymous, 4th Edition.* New York: A.A. World Services. p.85

Tools of Recovery

As recovering addicts, we have a wealth of tools of recovery at our disposal. These tools can help us stay clean and sober, maintain motivation to work our program, and help us create a better life for ourselves. This journal has been created around the following twelve tools:

Journaling

Journaling is simply writing down whatever's on our mind. It helps us clarify our thoughts and feelings, and can lead to acceptance of them. It can be especially useful when we feel overwhelmed by strong emotions, obsessive thoughts, or impulses toward our addiction. Simply writing about these things can often weaken their grip on us and allow us a better perspective.

Getting into the practice of journaling regularly offers us the opportunity to get in touch with the deeper parts of ourselves. Writing about our fears or our resentments can help bring these into the light of consciousness where they can be dealt with. Writing about our hopes and dreams can affirm these in our minds. It need only take a couple of minutes, and doing this is the morning can free our mind for the day ahead.

Gratitude

An attitude of gratitude helps us to live well. We can all get bogged down with the difficulties of life, especially in early recovery, but the simple truth is that even in the most dire times of despair, there are *always* things to be grateful for. A daily practice of making a list of some of the things we're grateful for brings balance to our lives. It prevents us losing sight of the positives, those things that provide nourishment. During difficult times, looking back through previous gratitude lists can quickly bring about a much needed boost.

Acceptance

*'God, grant me the serenity
to accept the things I cannot change;
courage to change the things I can;
and wisdom to know the difference* [1] *'*

Accepting the things we can't change is a central concept of the Twelve Step program, and its power cannot be overstated. Acceptance is an opening to the realities of life. If we don't accept, then we fight, struggle and resist, which holds us back and keeps us trapped.

By accepting life as it is, we can start to let go of guilt, shame and anger, begin to forgive others and ourselves, and change the direction of our lives. Throughout the journal, we're encouraged to jot one thing down each day that we need to accept.

Prayer & meditation

"Prayer and meditation are our principal means of conscious contact with God [2] *"*

These practices needn't be a stumbling block. There is no right or wrong way to pray or meditate, we each choose what is most meaningful to us. We choose both how to pray and the content of our prayers. Many recovering addicts regularly say The Serenity Prayer, as well as the prayers written in The Big Book of Alcoholics Anonymous.

There is a wealth of guidance and experience of meditative practices available to us, and recovery literature can provide valuable direction. Finding what works for each of us is the goal. What's important is that we make prayer and meditation a part of our lives.

---

1. Alcoholics Anonymous. (1995). *Twelve Steps and Twelve Traditions.* New York: Alcoholics Anonymous World Services. p.41

2. Alcoholics Anonymous. (1995). *Twelve Steps and Twelve Traditions.* New York: Alcoholics Anonymous World Services. p.96

Spiritual reading

Regularly reading recovery literature or spiritual material forms a foundation of many people's recoveries. When we spend a few minutes a day doing this, it keeps ideas of growth and recovery at the forefront of our minds. It helps us to incorporate spiritual concepts into our behaviours, and challenges us to think differently. Every fellowship has recommended literature available so there's plenty of choice.

Staying in touch with others in recovery

For many recovering addicts, the telephone is a lifeline. Staying connected to others in recovery strengthens us and brings us out of isolation. Sharing our thoughts and feelings with another nourishes us. Listening to someone else share theirs brings us out of 'self' and into the stream of life. Some people find this very hard to do at first, but as we gently settle into it, we find powerful benefits.

Some of us rigorously phone people every day, and some take a more *'as needed'* approach; some prefer meeting in person than speaking on the phone, others opt for text messages. None of us are better off without regular contact with others in recovery. There is space in this journal to write down and build up a list of people to stay in touch with. We'll be reminded on a daily basis to contact someone, and we'll be regularly prompted to review and update our list.

Service and helping others

Doing service and helping people can take many forms - helping set up the chairs at a meeting, doing outreach calls, listening to a friend or helping a neighbour with their shopping. But it's effects on our own wellbeing can be profound. Most of us report it gives us a sense of purpose and helps us gain perspective on our own issues. Helping others is known to have an immensely positive impact on our own health, happiness, and emotional wellbeing.

Exercise

Exercising helps us to take care of our physical and mental health. It invigorates us, lifts our spirits and keeps us away from our addictions. It's easily overlooked in recovery circles, but so many have found it a valuable support in maintaining sobriety/abstinence.

Exercising can be as simple as a brief walk or a few minutes of gentle stretching at home. Moderation and common sense are key here. The list of benefits we can experience if we open ourselves to exercising is practically endless.

One day at a time

"Just for today I will try to live trough this day only, and not tackle my whole life problem at once. I can do something for twelve hours that would appal me if I felt that I had to keep it up for a lifetime[1]"

Imagining we have to stay sober for the rest of our lives can be overwhelming for many of us. But the truth is we have no need to make grand pronouncements of *'never again'*, instead we just do it for today. We can manage to stay away from our addictions just for today. We can commit to using some of these tools of recovery just for today. This way, the challenge of recovery becomes more manageable. This journal has been created around the principle of *One day at a time.*

---

1. Alcoholics Anonymous. *Just for today.* York: General Service Board of Alcoholics Anonymous

Daily inventory

Another bedrock of the Twelve Step program is the practice of taking inventory at the end of each day. There are many ways to do this, and many of us don't manage to do it consistently for a variety of reasons. Daily inventories help us take stock, become conscious of our behaviours and help us correct course when necessary. This simple habit aids our growth and resilience. Throughout this journal, each day, we'll be prompted and guided through a personal inventory.

Attending meetings

Attending meetings helps us stay focussed on our recovery. They are a safe haven, where we can share each others experience, strength and hope. Most people find that when they are going through a difficult time or experiencing troubling thoughts and feelings, going to a meeting is the best thing to do. Reconnecting with other recovering addicts, and focussing on the common solution can be instantly transformative. Many people find that deciding at the beginning of the week which meetings they will attend helps them commit. Each week throughout the journal, we'll be given the opportunity to plan our meetings for the week ahead.

Looking at consequences

When in recovery, we can easily forget the consequences of our addictions. Such complacency can easily lead us to relapse. When faced with an impulse toward our addiction, it can be very helpful to think through the consequences. This can provide a quick and sobering reminder of where our addictive impulses lead us. In the next few pages, we're invited to briefly write about some of our experiences including our own *rock bottom,* and the potential consequences of a future relapse. We'll also be encouraged to regularly review these as we work through the journal, so they remain fresh in our minds. Having these already written down and accessible can be invaluable deterrents at times of vulnerability.

A note about honesty

For most, if not all of us, denial and deception were a foundation on which we built our lives of addiction. Conversely, rigorous honesty is what we build our recovery on. Getting honest is a process, and not an easy one for many of us. A good start can be getting honest with ourselves about what we're thinking and what we're feeling. Writing about this each day can aid us in this process, and each day we'll be given the opportunity to do so. Once we are used to being honest with ourselves about what's really going on inside, we'll find it easier to start opening up to others. The process of daily inventory also helps us get honest. By using this journal on a daily basis, we'll no longer be able to live in denial, we'll be able to see how well we're working the program, which aspects we're neglecting and where we need to focus our efforts.

Dear God,

I'm sorry about the mess I've made of my life.

I want to turn away from all the wrong things

I've ever done and all the wrong things I've ever been.

Please forgive me for it all.

I know You have the power to change my life

and can turn me into a winner.

Thank You, God for getting my attention long enough

to interest me in trying it Your way.

God, please take over the management of my life

and everything about me.

I am making this conscious decision to

turn my will and my life over to Your care

and am asking You to please

take over all parts of my life.

Please, God, move into my heart.

However You do it is Your business,

but make Yourself real inside me

and fill my awful emptiness.

Fill me with Your love and Holy Spirit

and make me know Your will for me.

And now, God, help Yourself to me and keep on doing it.

I'm not sure I want You to, but do it anyhow.

I rejoice that I am now a part of Your people,

that my uncertainty is gone forever,

and that You now have control of my will and my life.

Thank You and I praise Your name.

Amen

The Daily Pages

Journal

A space for us to write down whatever's on our mind. There are no rules here. Each day there is a different reflection at the top of the page - it's entirely optional whether or not we choose to write about this. For those of us not used to journaling, the reflection may help us get going with it

Sobriety Tracker

For those wishing to keep track of their sobriety/abstinence on a daily basis

Gratitude & acceptance

A space for us to reflect on these important principles of recovery

More tools of recover

This checklist will help us to incorporate the tools of recovery into our daily lives. We can each decide which tools to use on which days - we may want to circle the ones we plan to use that day, in the morning, and in the evening check off the ones we actually used. As the days and weeks go by, we'll be able to keep track of how well we're using the tools, and get a feel for where we might like to focus. Again, there are no rules here, no shoulds and shouldn'ts

Daily personal inventory

A core principle of twelve step programmes, and one that few manage to do consistently. The questions on each left-hand page are taken directly from *The Big Book of Alcoholics Anonymous*, whereas those on each right-hand page are alternatives you may wish to try. Some of us will want to stick to the *Big Book* questions, and some will welcome the variety

Daily planner

An opportunity to consciously plan the day ahead. Perhaps we may like to schedule in times to complete our recovery-related activities in amongst our other daily commitments

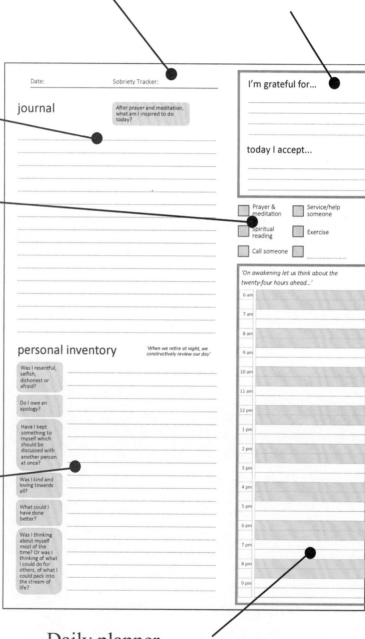

Date:

Sobriety Tracker:

journal

After prayer and meditation, what am I inspired to do today?

I'm grateful for...

today I accept...

☐ Prayer & meditation
☐ Service/help someone
☐ Spiritual reading
☐ Exercise
☐ Call someone
☐

'On awakening let us think about the twenty-four hours ahead...'

6 am
7 am
8 am
9 am
10 am
11 am
12 pm
1 pm
2 pm
3 pm
4 pm
5 pm
6 pm
7 pm
8 pm
9 pm

personal inventory

'When we retire at night, we constructively review our day'

Was I resentful, selfish, dishonest or afraid?

Do I owe an apology?

Have I kept something to myself which should be discussed with another person at once?

Was I kind and loving towards all?

What could I have done better?

Was I thinking about myself most of the time? Or was I thinking of what I could do for others, of what I could pack into the stream of life?

The Weekly Check-ins

Healthy reminders

To keep our motivation high, it's helpful to remind ourselves of some of the reasons we are in recovery, what can happen if we let our healthy habits slip, and how to get back on track if we do. Each week, we'll be prompted to re-read some of the worksheets we filled out at the front of the journal, so these things remain prominent in our minds

Reviewing the week

A chance for us to really think about the week just gone. Four questions here will encourage us to reflect on our successes, identify where we can improve, check in with our spirituality and think about how we want next week to be

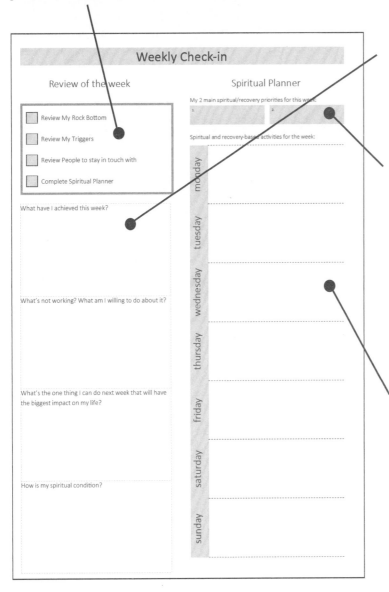

Focuses for next week

Having reviewed our week, we have a chance to identify our two main spiritual and recovery-based priorities for the week ahead. What have we been neglecting? What do we want to continue that's been working well? Is there something new we can commit to this week?

Spiritual planner

After reflecting on the week just gone, we now can start to plan out the week ahead, committing to our spiritual, recovery-based actions and activities. Which meetings will we go to? Who can we call? When shall we speak to our sponsor or sponsees? What have we been putting off that we can schedule in? What about looking after our physical health by getting some exercise? What else keeps us spiritually fit?

References

Throughout the journal, there are quotes from well known recovery literature. These show how this journal has been created based on well known recovery principles. Quotes are written in italics and can be identified on the References page at the back of the book

How to Use The 12 Step Journal

The 12 Step Journal uses a variety of techniques to help our recovery. The journal is made up of the following sections. Here we can see how best to use each section, and how they all fit together.

The Tools of Recovery

Here we have a look at the 12 tools of recovery that this journal has been built around. This is followed by some guidance on how to get the most out of the journal with a detailed look at the daily pages and the weekly check-ins.

The Clarity Worksheets

These 8 brief worksheets give us the opportunity to examine some key areas of our addiction and recovery. The purpose is to complete them once, carefully and honestly. At the end of each week, as we're working through the journal, we'll be prompted to review some of these worksheets. By doing this, we'll keep these important realities fresh in our minds, helping us to stay motivated and on track with our recovery activities. We can also update them where appropriate as we move ahead in our recovery and our understanding grows.

It's important not to get stuck on these worksheets, and not to delay starting the daily pages. Completing each worksheet shouldn't take long, and honesty is the key to success. Aim to complete them in the first week or two, but don't stress, you'll know when the time is right.

Reflections

A space to make note of and reflect on key insights that we gain as we spend time in recovery. Whether it's something we learn about ourselves while working through the steps, something that resonates with us while reading recovery literature, something we identify strongly with at a meeting or something we learn about our addiction, it's helpful to reflect on it while it's fresh in our mind.

Notes

Blank space to be used in whatever way is helpful for each of us.

Daily Pages

These are the main event. The daily pages ensure we stay focussed on our recovery, and help us to use the tools of recovery every day. Each day we have the opportunity to use up to 12 tools of recovery (see previous pages for details of these), as well as to plan our day and track our sobriety. These pages have been created to be the central hub of our recovery activities.

How much time we spend on it each day, when and how we use the journal is up to each of us.

Some of us, including people early in their recovery may want to start with just one or two parts of the daily pages, and build up from there. Some of us may find that some parts aren't yet relevant to us at our current stage in recovery. But all of us will be able to get benefit from the daily pages—the important thing is to get started and to use them consistently.

One way to use the daily pages would be:

Morning: We begin with prayer and meditation, and then with a clear mind we look ahead and plan our day. We do our daily reading and spend a minute thinking about what we've read. We write down what's on our mind, and use the daily reflection at the top of the page as food for thought. We decide how and if we are going to incorporate the other tools into our day, thinking about which ones would be most helpful for us that day. And we ask ourselves what we need to accept today.

Evening: At the end of the day, we complete our personal inventory and then tick off the tools we have used that day, making a quick note of which ones we may want to use tomorrow. Then we finish by jotting down some things we are grateful for from the day and in our lives generally.

By using the daily pages, we'll quickly be able to see how well we are working the program, and where we need to put in effort to improve. We'll quickly get a feel for which tools work well for us, and we'll continue learning about ourselves and our recovery.

These insights will be valuable and may form the basis of ongoing discussions with our sponsors or others in recovery.

Weekly Check-ins

Each week, we'll be given the opportunity to reflect back on the week, and to think about the week ahead. While this can be done on any day, we've found Sundays often work the best.

By reviewing the week as a whole, we'll be able to spot patterns and get a feel for our direction of travel. We'll be able to think about what has and hasn't worked well for us that week, and where we need to focus our attention moving forward. We'll be guided through this process. We'll also be asked to review some selected Clarity Worksheets that we completed at the beginning of the journal, helping us to keep an eye on the bigger picture of our recovery. We can then look ahead and set our intentions for the upcoming week.

Six-monthly Review

At the end of the journal, we'll be encouraged to reflect on our progress and celebrate our achievements. Reviewing our journey will be eye-opening and help us to launch into another period of grateful recovery.

References

Quotes from well known recovery literature appear throughout this journal. Quotes are in italics and often show how this book has been designed around established recovery philosophies. The References section at the back shows where these quotes originate from.

Lord, I want to love You, yet I am not sure.

I want to trust You, yet I am afraid of being taken in.

I know I need You, but I am ashamed of the need.

I want to pray, but I am afraid of being a hypocrite.

I need my independence, yet I fear to be alone.

I want to belong, yet I must be myself.

Take me Lord, yet leave me alone.

Lord, I believe; help me with my unbelief.

O Lord, if You are there, You do understand, don't You?

Give me what I need, but leave me free to choose.

Help me work it out my own way, but don't let me go.

Let me understand myself, but don't let me despair.

Come unto me, O Lord, I want You there.

Lighten my darkness, but don't dazzle me.

Help me to see what I need to do, and give me strength to do it.

O Lord, I believe; help me with my unbelief.

A Beginner's Prayer

Bill P. and Lisa D. *The 12 Step Prayer Book. 2nd ed.* Center City, Minn.: Hazelden, 2004

Clarity Worksheets

My Rock Bottom

We all have our rock bottom – that moment that finally breaks us, where we start to seek a better way. Many of us are extremely grateful for hitting ours when we did, as it led us to recovery and the start of our new lives. Reflecting on our rock bottom is powerful and useful in a number of ways: it reminds us how bad things can get and where our addictions can take us; it shows us how far we have come since our recovery began; it allows us to learn valuable personal life lessons and glean insights from our experiences; and it helps keep us from falling into complacency with our recovery.

Take some time now to describe your personal rock bottom. Details are helpful. What was happening? What were your behaviours? How were you feeling? What was the impact on others in your life? What were your thoughts at the time? What risks were you taking? How were you justifying your addictive behaviours? How was your physical health? What was your financial situation like? What were your relationships like? What would have happened if you hadn't have started your recovery? What did you learn about yourself?

What are my triggers?

Identifying and understanding our personal relapse triggers is one of the most important techniques for preventing a relapse. We all have triggers, and if we don't know what ours are, then we won't be able to avoid or manage them. Take the time now to think through and jot down your personal triggers, those things that make you more likely to turn to your addictive behaviour. It might be helpful to break them down:

⇒   Emotional triggers e.g. frustration, stress, anger, sadness, loneliness, guilt, even positive emotions like elation and excitement

⇒   Environmental triggers — places or objects that you associate with your addictive behaviour

⇒   Social triggers i.e. specific people or situations

What would happen if I relapse?

Use this space to list all the consequences you'd face if you were to relapse into addiction. What would you lose? What would you be risking? What would happen to your relationships? How would your work or career be affected? What would happen to your finances? How would other people in your life be affected? What would happen to your physical health? Your mental health? Who, besides yourself, would you be hurting? Would you be risking your home? Your freedom? Your life?

Regularly reviewing this page can help to stay motivated with daily recovery activities.

My vision for the future

We've looked at what would happen if you were to relapse, and the direction your addiction(s) would take your life. Now let's change focus and think about how your life can be with ongoing recovery. Recovery isn't just about avoiding the bad, but also living the good. This is a time to think about how you want your life to be, how your higher power would have you be. What would a happy, fulfilling life look like for you?

Thinking about an ideal future for yourself, what things would you choose? How would you feel each day? What kind of thoughts and emotions would you choose to have? How would your work/career be? What would your love life look like? What kind of relationships would you have with others in your life? How would your work-life balance be? How would you be contributing to the wellbeing of others? What would other people say about you? How would your health be? What about your social life? Your finances? What kind of environment would you live in? How would you make a difference? Would you have hobbies? Creative pursuits?

How I'll know if I'm heading for a relapse

It can be difficult for us to spot in ourselves when we may be heading towards a relapse into our addiction. It's often only afterwards, when we look back on a relapse that we can see what was really happening. And often those around us can spot the warning signs long before we can. Our ability to know we're heading for trouble usually grows gradually as we spend longer in recovery. Being able to spot the warning signs early can really help us avert some potential disasters, so the time you spend on this page really will be time well spent.

Thinking objectively about your experiences in addiction, and those of other recovering addicts, answer the following questions as best you can. What are your thoughts likely to be in the lead up to a relapse? Romanticising the good old days of active addiction? Thinking 'one more time won't hurt'? Are you likely to be obsessing over unimportant things? How are you likely to be feeling? Stressed? Bored? Lonely? Agitated? Overwhelmed? Frustrated? What behaviours are you likely to *start* exhibiting? Will you start becoming defensive or angry with people? Will you start reconnecting with people associated with your addiction? Will you engage in compulsive behaviours? What behaviours are you likely to *stop*? Going to meetings perhaps? Putting off step work? Withdrawing from your support network perhaps? Avoiding your sponsor? Will you stop praying and meditating? Are you likely to stop taking care of yourself? Will you let your daily routine slip? What kinds of things will your loved ones and people around you be saying to you?

My Rescue Plan

Now we've identified how you'll know that you're heading towards a relapse, it's time to formulate a plan that you can follow when you're in that danger zone, or when you've had a slip. The following are suggestions to help you get back on track, so think through which of them could be helpful, and add some more of your own.

Speak honestly with someone – which people could you call or speak to? Go to a meeting. Pray – surrender, ask for help/strength/motivation. Read recovery literature. Read other spiritual or uplifting material. Remove particular temptations from your environment. Challenge your thoughts and rationalisations. Think through the consequences of a relapse – re-read the 'What will happen if I relapse' worksheet. Re-read 'My Rock Bottom' and 'My vision for the future'. Help someone. Exercise. How else could you re-commit to your recovery? Speak to others in recovery for ideas.

My Character Defects

As we work through the steps and gain time in recovery, we come to understand ourselves better. Part of this involves gaining clarity on our defects of character—those qualities of our personality which cause us difficulties. As our recovery progresses, our self-understanding grows, and it can serve us well to keep our character defects fresh in our minds. So use this space to list yours, and add to it as new insights emerge. You'll be prompted to regularly review this list as you progress through the journal.

People to stay in touch with

Living in addiction usually isolates us. And this isolation feeds the addiction in a vicious cycle. Staying connected to people is an essential pillar in our recovery, one that can be all too easy to neglect, especially when we are feeling vulnerable. Use this page to list the people who make up your support network – those who maintaining a relationship with benefits you both. You may want to note their phone numbers as well. Keep adding to the list as other people come into your life. Maintaining this list reminds us to stay connected, you'll be prompted to review and update it as you work through the journal. Take these opportunities to think about those you could reach out to.

God grant me the serenity to accept my addiction gracefully and humbly. Grant me also the ability to absorb the teachings of the Program, which by its past experience is trying to help me. Teach me to be grateful for the help I receive.

Guide me, *Higher Power*, in the path of tolerance and understanding of my fellow members and fellowman, guide me away from the path of criticism, intolerance, jealousy, and envy of my friends. Let me not prejudge; let me not become a moralist; keep my tongue and thoughts from malicious, idle gossip.

Help me to grow in stature spiritually, mentally, and morally. Grant me that greatest of all rewards, that of being able to help my fellow sufferers in their search out of the addiction that has encompassed them.

Above all, help me to be less critical and impatient with myself.

The Acceptance Prayer
Bill P. and Lisa D. *The 12 Step Prayer Book. 2nd ed.* Center City, Minn.: Hazelden, 2004

Reflections

Reflections

As we recover, our minds clear and we become open to new insights, new ways of thinking and new perspectives. These can come to us during meetings, while reading literature, working through the steps, in conversation with others in recovery or our sponsors, in prayer or meditation, or in any number of ways. But they do come to us, and they come often. Perhaps we identify with the experiences shared by another at a meeting, or we spot a recurring pattern of behaviour in ourselves while working on our moral inventory, or a piece of literature resonates with us on a deep level.

The next 10 pages gives us an opportunity to make a note of our new insights as they come up, and to reflect on them. Why are they important to us? What are they telling us? What changes do we need to make?

Lord, make me a channel of thy peace;

That where there is hatred, I may bring love;

That where there is wrong, I may bring the spirit of forgiveness;

That where there is discord, I may bring harmony;

That where there is error, I may bring truth;

That where there is doubt, I may bring faith;

That where there is despair, I may bring hope;

That where there are shadows, I may bring light;

That where there is sadness, I may bring joy.

Lord, grant that I may seek rather to comfort than to be comforted;

To understand, than to be understood;

To love, than to be loved.

For it is by self-forgetting that one finds.

It is by forgiving that one is forgiven.

It is by dying that one awakens to Eternal Life.

Amen

Prayer of Saint Francis of Assisi

Alcoholics Anonymous. (1995). Twelve Steps and Twelve Traditions. New York: Alcoholics Anonymous World Services. p.99

Notes

Notes

Today I pray that I can:

Take time to think.
　　　It is the source of power.

Take time to play.
　　　It is the secret of perpetual youth.

Take time to read.
　　　It is the fountain of wisdom.

Take time to pray.
　　　It is the greatest power on earth.

Take time to be friendly.
　　　It is the road to happiness.

Take time to laugh.
　　　It is the music of the soul.

Take time to give.
　　　It is too short a day to be selfish.

Take time to work.
　　　It is the price of success.

Take time to do charity.
　　　It is the key to heaven.

Take Time

Bill P. and Lisa D. *The 12 Step Prayer Book. 2nd ed.* Center City, Minn.: Hazelden, 2004

Daily Toolkit Pages

journal

How can I be a better friend?

_____
_____
_____
_____
_____
_____
_____
_____
_____
_____
_____
_____
_____

personal inventory

'When we retire at night, we constructively review our day'

Was I resentful, selfish, dishonest or afraid?	....
Do I owe an apology?	....
Have I kept something to myself which should be discussed with another person at once?	....
Was I kind and loving towards all?	....
What could I have done better?	....
Was I thinking about myself most of the time? Or was I thinking of what I could do for others, of what I could pack into the stream of life?	....

I'm grateful for...

_____
_____
_____
_____

today I accept...

_____
_____
_____

☐ Prayer & meditation   ☐ Service/help someone

☐ Spiritual reading   ☐ Exercise

☐ Call someone   ☐ ....

'On awakening let us think about the twenty-four hours ahead...'

6 am	
7 am	
8 am	
9 am	
10 am	
11 am	
12 pm	
1 pm	
2 pm	
3 pm	
4 pm	
5 pm	
6 pm	
7 pm	
8 pm	
9 pm	

'A genuine gratitude for blessings received'

....
....
....
....

'God, grant me the serenity to accept the things I cannot change'

....
....
....
....

- ☐ Prayer & meditation
- ☐ Service/help someone
- ☐ Spiritual reading
- ☐ Exercise
- ☐ Call someone
- ☐ ....

'...We consider our plans for the day'

	6 am
	7 am
	8 am
	9 am
	10 am
	11 am
	12 pm
	1 pm
	2 pm
	3 pm
	4 pm
	5 pm
	6 pm
	7 pm
	8 pm
	9 pm

journal

Which of the tools in the checklist will best serve me today?

....
....
....
....
....
....
....
....
....
....
....
....
....
....

personal inventory

'When we retire at night, we constructively review our day'

Was I unkind (cruel, harsh, unfeeling)?

Who did I help today?

How did I show love to myself? Did I talk negatively to myself?

Am I obsessing about anything?

What am I proud of today?

Was I patient, kind and compassionate? What caused me to lose these attitudes? Do I owe anyone amends?

Date: _____ Sobriety Tracker: _____

journal

What's the best advice I've ever received?

_____
_____
_____
_____
_____
_____
_____
_____
_____
_____
_____
_____
_____
_____
_____
_____
_____

I'm grateful for...

_____
_____
_____
_____

today I accept...

_____
_____
_____

☐ Prayer & meditation   ☐ Service/help someone

☐ Spiritual reading   ☐ Exercise

☐ Call someone   ☐ ....

'On awakening let us think about the twenty-four hours ahead...'

6 am
7 am
8 am
9 am
10 am
11 am
12 pm
1 pm
2 pm
3 pm
4 pm
5 pm
6 pm
7 pm
8 pm
9 pm

personal inventory

'When we retire at night, we constructively review our day'

Was I resentful, selfish, dishonest or afraid?

Do I owe an apology?

Have I kept something to myself which should be discussed with another person at once?

Was I kind and loving towards all?

What could I have done better?

Was I thinking about myself most of the time? Or was I thinking of what I could do for others, of what I could pack into the stream of life?

'A genuine gratitude for blessings received'

....
....
....
....

'God, grant me the serenity to accept the things I cannot change'

....
....
....

☐	Prayer & meditation	☐	Service/help someone
☐	Spiritual reading	☐	Exercise
☐	Call someone	☐	....

'...We consider our plans for the day'

	6 am
	7 am
	8 am
	9 am
	10 am
	11 am
	12 pm
	1 pm
	2 pm
	3 pm
	4 pm
	5 pm
	6 pm
	7 pm
	8 pm
	9 pm

journal

What would I love to experience just for fun?

....
....
....
....
....
....
....
....
....
....
....
....
....

personal inventory

'When we retire at night, we constructively review our day'

Did I do something for someone else today?

What did I accomplish today?

What have I done for my recovery today?

Am I taking care of my body?

What could I have done better?

Was I unloving today (cold, unresponsive, indifferent)?

Date: _____   Sobriety Tracker: _____

journal

> What's the biggest risk I've taken?

_____
_____
_____
_____
_____
_____
_____
_____
_____
_____
_____
_____
_____

personal inventory

'When we retire at night, we constructively review our day'

Was I resentful, selfish, dishonest or afraid?
_____

Do I owe an apology?
_____

Have I kept something to myself which should be discussed with another person at once?
_____

Was I kind and loving towards all?
_____

What could I have done better?
_____

Was I thinking about myself most of the time? Or was I thinking of what I could do for others, of what I could pack into the stream of life?
_____

I'm grateful for...
_____
_____
_____

today I accept...
_____
_____

- [ ] Prayer & meditation
- [ ] Service/help someone
- [ ] Spiritual reading
- [ ] Exercise
- [ ] Call someone
- [ ] ....

'On awakening let us think about the twenty-four hours ahead...'

6 am	
7 am	
8 am	
9 am	
10 am	
11 am	
12 pm	
1 pm	
2 pm	
3 pm	
4 pm	
5 pm	
6 pm	
7 pm	
8 pm	
9 pm	

'A genuine gratitude for blessings received'

....
....
....
....

'God, grant me the serenity to accept the things I cannot change'

....
....
....
....

☐ Prayer & meditation   ☐ Service/help someone

☐ Spiritual reading   ☐ Exercise

☐ Call someone   ☐ ....

'...We consider our plans for the day'

	6 am
	7 am
	8 am
	9 am
	10 am
	11 am
	12 pm
	1 pm
	2 pm
	3 pm
	4 pm
	5 pm
	6 pm
	7 pm
	8 pm
	9 pm

journal

> What new skills would I like to develop?

....
....
....
....
....
....
....
....
....
....
....
....

personal inventory

'When we retire at night, we constructively review our day'

Was I honest with others and myself today?
....

What can I celebrate? What could I have done differently?
....

How was my serenity? Did anything happen that caused me to lose it? What was my part in it?
....

Am I spending time on myself?
....

What did I do to connect with my higher power?
....

Did fear prevent me from doing anything today?
....

Date: _____   Sobriety Tracker: _____

journal

What's on my mind?
What's in my heart?

_____
_____
_____
_____
_____
_____
_____
_____
_____
_____
_____
_____
_____
_____

personal inventory

'When we retire at night, we constructively review our day'

Was I resentful, selfish, dishonest or afraid?
_____

Do I owe an apology?
_____

Have I kept something to myself which should be discussed with another person at once?
_____

Was I kind and loving towards all?
_____

What could I have done better?
_____

Was I thinking about myself most of the time? Or was I thinking of what I could do for others, of what I could pack into the stream of life?
_____

I'm grateful for...

_____
_____
_____
_____

today I accept...

_____
_____

☐ Prayer & meditation   ☐ Service/help someone

☐ Spiritual reading   ☐ Exercise

☐ Call someone   ☐ ....

'On awakening let us think about the twenty-four hours ahead...'

6 am
7 am
8 am
9 am
10 am
11 am
12 pm
1 pm
2 pm
3 pm
4 pm
5 pm
6 pm
7 pm
8 pm
9 pm

Weekly Check-in

Review of the week

- [ ] Review My Rock Bottom
- [ ] Review My Character Defects
- [ ] Review People to stay in touch with
- [ ] Complete Spiritual Planner

What have I achieved this week?

What's not working? What am I willing to do about it?

What one thing can I do next week that will have the biggest positive impact on my life?

What do I need to make a decision about?

Spiritual Planner

My 2 main spiritual/recovery priorities for this week:

1.

2.

Spiritual and recovery-based activities for the week:

monday

tuesday

wednesday

thursday

friday

saturday

sunday

journal

Is there anyone who I need to give a second chance to?

I'm grateful for...

today I accept...

☐ Prayer & meditation   ☐ Service/help someone

☐ Spiritual reading   ☐ Exercise

☐ Call someone   ☐ ....

'On awakening let us think about the twenty-four hours ahead...'

6 am
7 am
8 am
9 am
10 am
11 am
12 pm
1 pm
2 pm
3 pm
4 pm
5 pm
6 pm
7 pm
8 pm
9 pm

personal inventory

'When we retire at night, we constructively review our day'

Was I resentful, selfish, dishonest or afraid?

Do I owe an apology?

Have I kept something to myself which should be discussed with another person at once?

Was I kind and loving towards all?

What could I have done better?

Was I thinking about myself most of the time? Or was I thinking of what I could do for others, of what I could pack into the stream of life?

'A genuine gratitude for blessings received'

_____
_____
_____
_____

'God, grant me the serenity to accept the things I cannot change'

_____
_____
_____

☐ Prayer & meditation   ☐ Service/help someone

☐ Spiritual reading   ☐ Exercise

☐ Call someone   ☐ ....

'...We consider our plans for the day'

	6 am
	7 am
	8 am
	9 am
	10 am
	11 am
	12 pm
	1 pm
	2 pm
	3 pm
	4 pm
	5 pm
	6 pm
	7 pm
	8 pm
	9 pm

Date: _____   Sobriety Tracker: _____

journal

Who do I need to set healthy boundaries with?

_____
_____
_____
_____
_____
_____
_____
_____
_____
_____
_____
_____
_____

personal inventory

'When we retire at night, we constructively review our day'

Have I practiced any of my character defects?
_____

Am I keeping any secrets?
_____

Was I honest? Did I keep my word with everyone? Did I keep my word with myself?
_____

Am I trying to fill the void with external stimuli?
_____

Did I learn something useful today? Or was I a mental loafer?
_____

Was I concerned today with thoughts or behaviours linked to my addiction?
_____

Date: _____ Sobriety Tracker: _____

journal

Who have I been avoiding? Why?

_____
_____
_____
_____
_____
_____
_____
_____
_____
_____
_____
_____
_____
_____
_____
_____

personal inventory

'When we retire at night, we constructively review our day'

Was I resentful, selfish, dishonest or afraid?
_____
_____

Do I owe an apology?
_____
_____

Have I kept something to myself which should be discussed with another person at once?
_____
_____
_____

Was I kind and loving towards all?
_____
_____

What could I have done better?
_____
_____

Was I thinking about myself most of the time? Or was I thinking of what I could do for others, of what I could pack into the stream of life?
_____
_____
_____
_____

I'm grateful for...

_____
_____
_____
_____

today I accept...

_____
_____
_____

☐ Prayer & meditation   ☐ Service/help someone

☐ Spiritual reading   ☐ Exercise

☐ Call someone   ☐ ....

'On awakening let us think about the twenty-four hours ahead...'

6 am
7 am
8 am
9 am
10 am
11 am
12 pm
1 pm
2 pm
3 pm
4 pm
5 pm
6 pm
7 pm
8 pm
9 pm

'A genuine gratitude for blessings received'

....
....
....
....

'God, grant me the serenity to accept the things I cannot change'

....
....
....
....

☐ Prayer & meditation   ☐ Service/help someone

☐ Spiritual reading   ☐ Exercise

☐ Call someone   ☐ ....

'...We consider our plans for the day'

6 am	
7 am	
8 am	
9 am	
10 am	
11 am	
12 pm	
1 pm	
2 pm	
3 pm	
4 pm	
5 pm	
6 pm	
7 pm	
8 pm	
9 pm	

journal

What baggage do I have that holds me back?

....
....
....
....
....
....
....
....
....
....
....
....
....
....

personal inventory

'When we retire at night, we constructively review our day'

How did I take care of my health (physical, emotional, spiritual) today?

What have I enjoyed about today?

How did I show love to others? Did I act unlovingly towards anyone?

Who neds my prayers today?

Am I holding any resentments?

How is my spiritual condition?

Date: _____ Sobriety Tracker: _____

journal

What nourishes my soul?

_____
_____
_____
_____
_____
_____
_____
_____
_____
_____
_____
_____
_____

personal inventory

'When we retire at night, we constructively review our day'

Was I resentful, selfish, dishonest or afraid?
_____

Do I owe an apology?
_____

Have I kept something to myself which should be discussed with another person at once?
_____

Was I kind and loving towards all?
_____

What could I have done better?
_____

Was I thinking about myself most of the time? Or was I thinking of what I could do for others, of what I could pack into the stream of life?
_____

I'm grateful for...

_____
_____
_____
_____

today I accept...

_____
_____
_____

- [ ] Prayer & meditation
- [ ] Service/help someone
- [ ] Spiritual reading
- [ ] Exercise
- [ ] Call someone
- [ ] _____

'On awakening let us think about the twenty-four hours ahead...'

6 am
7 am
8 am
9 am
10 am
11 am
12 pm
1 pm
2 pm
3 pm
4 pm
5 pm
6 pm
7 pm
8 pm
9 pm

'A genuine gratitude for blessings received'

....
....
....
....

'God, grant me the serenity to accept the things I cannot change'

....
....
....
....

- ☐ Prayer & meditation
- ☐ Service/help someone
- ☐ Spiritual reading
- ☐ Exercise
- ☐ Call someone
- ☐ ....

'...We consider our plans for the day'

	6 am
	7 am
	8 am
	9 am
	10 am
	11 am
	12 pm
	1 pm
	2 pm
	3 pm
	4 pm
	5 pm
	6 pm
	7 pm
	8 pm
	9 pm

journal

How can I be more loving towards the people in my life?

....
....
....
....
....
....
....
....
....
....
....
....
....
....
....

personal inventory

'When we retire at night, we constructively review our day'

Was I unkind (cruel, harsh, unfeeling)?
....
....

Who did I help today?
....
....

How did I show love to myself? Did I talk negatively to myself?
....
....

Am I obsessing about anything?
....
....

What am I proud of today?
....
....

Was I patient, kind and compassionate? What caused me to lose these attitudes? Do I owe anyone amends?
....
....
....
....

Date: _____ Sobriety Tracker: _____

journal

> How can I contribute more to the wellbeing of others?

_____
_____
_____
_____
_____
_____
_____
_____
_____
_____
_____
_____
_____

personal inventory

'When we retire at night, we constructively review our day'

Was I resentful, selfish, dishonest or afraid?
_____

Do I owe an apology?
_____

Have I kept something to myself which should be discussed with another person at once?
_____
_____
_____

Was I kind and loving towards all?
_____

What could I have done better?
_____

Was I thinking about myself most of the time? Or was I thinking of what I could do for others, of what I could pack into the stream of life?
_____
_____
_____
_____

I'm grateful for...

_____
_____
_____

today I accept...

_____
_____

☐ Prayer & meditation   ☐ Service/help someone

☐ Spiritual reading   ☐ Exercise

☐ Call someone   ☐ ....

'On awakening let us think about the twenty-four hours ahead...'

6 am	
7 am	
8 am	
9 am	
10 am	
11 am	
12 pm	
1 pm	
2 pm	
3 pm	
4 pm	
5 pm	
6 pm	
7 pm	
8 pm	
9 pm	

Weekly Check-in

Review of the week

Review My Triggers

Review My Rescue Plan

Review People to stay in touch with

Complete Spiritual Planner

What's working and why is it working?

What part of my recovery have I been neglecting?

What do I need to pay more attention to?

Have I had fun this week? How can I have more fun?

Spiritual Planner

My 2 main spiritual/recovery priorities for this week:

1.

2.

Spiritual and recovery-based activities for the week:

monday

tuesday

wednesday

thursday

friday

saturday

sunday

Date: _____   Sobriety Tracker: _____

journal

> What fears do I have at the moment?

....
....
....
....
....
....
....
....
....
....
....
....

I'm grateful for...

....
....
....
....

today I accept...

....
....
....

☐ Prayer & meditation   ☐ Service/help someone

☐ Spiritual reading   ☐ Exercise

☐ Call someone   ☐ ....

'On awakening let us think about the twenty-four hours ahead...'

6 am	
7 am	
8 am	
9 am	
10 am	
11 am	
12 pm	
1 pm	
2 pm	
3 pm	
4 pm	
5 pm	
6 pm	
7 pm	
8 pm	
9 pm	

personal inventory

'When we retire at night, we constructively review our day'

Was I resentful, selfish, dishonest or afraid?
....

Do I owe an apology?
....

Have I kept something to myself which should be discussed with another person at once?
....

Was I kind and loving towards all?
....

What could I have done better?
....

Was I thinking about myself most of the time? Or was I thinking of what I could do for others, of what I could pack into the stream of life?
....

'A genuine gratitude for blessings received'

_____
_____
_____

'God, grant me the serenity to accept the things I cannot change'

_____
_____
_____

- ☐ Prayer & meditation
- ☐ Service/help someone
- ☐ Spiritual reading
- ☐ Exercise
- ☐ Call someone
- ☐ ....

'...We consider our plans for the day'

	6 am
	7 am
	8 am
	9 am
	10 am
	11 am
	12 pm
	1 pm
	2 pm
	3 pm
	4 pm
	5 pm
	6 pm
	7 pm
	8 pm
	9 pm

journal

Was there a turning point in my life?

personal inventory

'When we retire at night, we constructively review our day'

Did I do something for someone else today?

What did I accomplish today?

What have I done for my recovery today?

Am I taking care of my body?

What could I have done better?

Was I unloving today (cold, unresponsive, indifferent)?

Date: _____ Sobriety Tracker: _____

journal

> What am I feeling right now?

_____
_____
_____
_____
_____
_____
_____
_____
_____
_____
_____
_____
_____
_____

personal inventory

'When we retire at night, we constructively review our day'

Was I resentful, selfish, dishonest or afraid?
_____

Do I owe an apology?
_____

Have I kept something to myself which should be discussed with another person at once?
_____

Was I kind and loving towards all?
_____

What could I have done better?
_____

Was I thinking about myself most of the time? Or was I thinking of what I could do for others, of what I could pack into the stream of life?
_____

I'm grateful for...

_____
_____
_____

today I accept...

_____
_____

- ☐ Prayer & meditation
- ☐ Service/help someone
- ☐ Spiritual reading
- ☐ Exercise
- ☐ Call someone
- ☐ ....

'On awakening let us think about the twenty-four hours ahead...'

6 am	
7 am	
8 am	
9 am	
10 am	
11 am	
12 pm	
1 pm	
2 pm	
3 pm	
4 pm	
5 pm	
6 pm	
7 pm	
8 pm	
9 pm	

'A genuine gratitude for blessings received'

....

....

....

....

'God, grant me the serenity to accept the things I cannot change'

....

....

....

☐ Prayer & meditation   ☐ Service/help someone

☐ Spiritual reading   ☐ Exercise

☐ Call someone   ☐ ....

'...We consider our plans for the day'

	6 am
	7 am
	8 am
	9 am
	10 am
	11 am
	12 pm
	1 pm
	2 pm
	3 pm
	4 pm
	5 pm
	6 pm
	7 pm
	8 pm
	9 pm

Date: _____   Sobriety Tracker: _____

journal

How can I be more helpful to those around me?

....

....

....

....

....

....

....

....

....

....

....

....

personal inventory

'When we retire at night, we constructively review our day'

Was I honest with others and myself today?

What can I celebrate? What could I have done differently?

How was my serenity? Did anything happen that caused me to lose it? What was my part in it?

Am I spending time on myself?

What did I do to connect with my higher power?

Did fear prevent me from doing anything today?

Date: _____   Sobriety Tracker: _____

journal

> What new hobby or sport would I like to start?

_____
_____
_____
_____
_____
_____
_____
_____
_____
_____
_____
_____
_____
_____

personal inventory

'When we retire at night, we constructively review our day'

Was I resentful, selfish, dishonest or afraid?	....
Do I owe an apology?	....
Have I kept something to myself which should be discussed with another person at once?	....
Was I kind and loving towards all?	....
What could I have done better?	....
Was I thinking about myself most of the time? Or was I thinking of what I could do for others, of what I could pack into the stream of life?	....

I'm grateful for...

_____
_____
_____

today I accept...

_____
_____
_____

☐ Prayer & meditation   ☐ Service/help someone

☐ Spiritual reading   ☐ Exercise

☐ Call someone   ☐ ....

'On awakening let us think about the twenty-four hours ahead...'

6 am
7 am
8 am
9 am
10 am
11 am
12 pm
1 pm
2 pm
3 pm
4 pm
5 pm
6 pm
7 pm
8 pm
9 pm

'A genuine gratitude for blessings received'

_____

'God, grant me the serenity to accept the things I cannot change'

_____

- ☐ Prayer & meditation
- ☐ Service/help someone
- ☐ Spiritual reading
- ☐ Exercise
- ☐ Call someone
- ☐ ....

'...We consider our plans for the day'

- 6 am
- 7 am
- 8 am
- 9 am
- 10 am
- 11 am
- 12 pm
- 1 pm
- 2 pm
- 3 pm
- 4 pm
- 5 pm
- 6 pm
- 7 pm
- 8 pm
- 9 pm

Date: _____ Sobriety Tracker: _____

journal

What period of my life did I like the most? Why?

_____

personal inventory

'When we retire at night, we constructively review our day'

Have I practiced any of my character defects?

Am I keeping any secrets?

Was I honest? Did I keep my word with everyone? Did I keep my word with myself?

Am I trying to fill the void with external stimuli?

Did I learn something useful today? Or was I a mental loafer?

Was I concerned today with thoughts or behaviours linked to my addiction?

Date: _____ Sobriety Tracker: _____

journal

Do I say 'yes' or 'no' more often?

....
....
....
....
....
....
....
....
....
....
....
....
....
....

personal inventory

'When we retire at night, we constructively review our day'

Was I resentful, selfish, dishonest or afraid?
....
....

Do I owe an apology?
....
....

Have I kept something to myself which should be discussed with another person at once?
....
....
....
....

Was I kind and loving towards all?
....
....

What could I have done better?
....
....

Was I thinking about myself most of the time? Or was I thinking of what I could do for others, of what I could pack into the stream of life?
....
....
....
....
....

I'm grateful for...
....
....
....
....

today I accept...
....
....

☐ Prayer & meditation   ☐ Service/help someone

☐ Spiritual reading   ☐ Exercise

☐ Call someone   ☐ ....

'On awakening let us think about the twenty-four hours ahead...'

6 am
7 am
8 am
9 am
10 am
11 am
12 pm
1 pm
2 pm
3 pm
4 pm
5 pm
6 pm
7 pm
8 pm
9 pm

Weekly Check-in

Review of the week

- Review What would happen if I relapse
- Review My Character Defects
- Review People to stay in touch with
- Complete Spiritual Planner

What's made me happy this week?

What's been most difficult this week? Do I need to change something?

What do I need to start doing? What do I need to stop doing?

How can I prioritise my time better?

Spiritual Planner

My 2 main spiritual/recovery priorities for this week:

1.

2.

Spiritual and recovery-based activities for the week:

monday

tuesday

wednesday

thursday

friday

saturday

sunday

journal

What have I been putting off that I really should face?

personal inventory

'When we retire at night, we constructively review our day'

Was I resentful, selfish, dishonest or afraid?

Do I owe an apology?

Have I kept something to myself which should be discussed with another person at once?

Was I kind and loving towards all?

What could I have done better?

Was I thinking about myself most of the time? Or was I thinking of what I could do for others, of what I could pack into the stream of life?

I'm grateful for...

today I accept...

- [ ] Prayer & meditation
- [ ] Service/help someone
- [ ] Spiritual reading
- [ ] Exercise
- [ ] Call someone
- [ ] ....

'On awakening let us think about the twenty-four hours ahead...'

6 am

7 am

8 am

9 am

10 am

11 am

12 pm

1 pm

2 pm

3 pm

4 pm

5 pm

6 pm

7 pm

8 pm

9 pm

'A genuine gratitude for blessings received'

....
....
....
....

'God, grant me the serenity to accept the things I cannot change'

....
....
....
....

journal

> After prayer and meditation, what am I inspired to do today?

☐ Prayer & meditation ☐ Service/help someone

☐ Spiritual reading ☐ Exercise

☐ Call someone ☐ ....

'...We consider our plans for the day'

	6 am
	7 am
	8 am
	9 am
	10 am
	11 am
	12 pm
	1 pm
	2 pm
	3 pm
	4 pm
	5 pm
	6 pm
	7 pm
	8 pm
	9 pm

personal inventory

'When we retire at night, we constructively review our day'

How did I take care of my health (physical, emotional, spiritual) today?

What have I enjoyed about today?

How did I show love to others? Did I act unlovingly towards anyone?

Who neds my prayers today?

Am I holding any resentments?

How is my spiritual condition?

Date: _____ Sobriety Tracker: _____

journal

How open am I with others?

_____
_____
_____
_____
_____
_____
_____
_____
_____
_____
_____
_____
_____
_____

personal inventory

'When we retire at night, we constructively review our day'

Was I resentful, selfish, dishonest or afraid?	_____
Do I owe an apology?	_____
Have I kept something to myself which should be discussed with another person at once?	_____
Was I kind and loving towards all?	_____
What could I have done better?	_____
Was I thinking about myself most of the time? Or was I thinking of what I could do for others, of what I could pack into the stream of life?	_____

I'm grateful for...

_____
_____
_____

today I accept...

_____
_____
_____

☐ Prayer & meditation   ☐ Service/help someone

☐ Spiritual reading   ☐ Exercise

☐ Call someone   ☐

'On awakening let us think about the twenty-four hours ahead...'

6 am	
7 am	
8 am	
9 am	
10 am	
11 am	
12 pm	
1 pm	
2 pm	
3 pm	
4 pm	
5 pm	
6 pm	
7 pm	
8 pm	
9 pm	

A genuine gratitude for blessings received'

....

....

....

'God, grant me the serenity to accept the things I cannot change'

....

....

....

☐ Prayer & meditation

☐ Service/help someone

☐ Spiritual reading

☐ Exercise

☐ Call someone

☐ ....

'...We consider our plans for the day'

6 am	
7 am	
8 am	
9 am	
10 am	
11 am	
12 pm	
1 pm	
2 pm	
3 pm	
4 pm	
5 pm	
6 pm	
7 pm	
8 pm	
9 pm	

Date: _____   Sobriety Tracker: _____

journal

What's my favourite time of day? Why?

....

....

....

....

....

....

....

....

....

....

....

....

personal inventory

'When we retire at night, we constructively review our day'

Was I unkind (cruel, harsh, unfeeling)?

Who did I help today?

How did I show love to myself? Did I talk negatively to myself?

Am I obsessing about anything?

What am I proud of today?

Was I patient, kind and compassionate? What caused me to lose these attitudes? Do I owe anyone amends?

Date: _____ Sobriety Tracker: _____

journal

How do I want to be today?

_____
_____
_____
_____
_____
_____
_____
_____
_____
_____
_____
_____
_____
_____
_____

personal inventory

'When we retire at night, we constructively review our day'

Was I resentful, selfish, dishonest or afraid?	_____
Do I owe an apology?	_____
Have I kept something to myself which should be discussed with another person at once?	_____
Was I kind and loving towards all?	_____
What could I have done better?	_____
Was I thinking about myself most of the time? Or was I thinking of what I could do for others, of what I could pack into the stream of life?	_____

I'm grateful for...

_____
_____
_____

today I accept...

_____
_____
_____

☐ Prayer & meditation   ☐ Service/help someone

☐ Spiritual reading   ☐ Exercise

☐ Call someone   ☐ _____

'On awakening let us think about the twenty-four hours ahead...'

6 am	
7 am	
8 am	
9 am	
10 am	
11 am	
12 pm	
1 pm	
2 pm	
3 pm	
4 pm	
5 pm	
6 pm	
7 pm	
8 pm	
9 pm	

'A genuine gratitude for blessings received'

_____
_____
_____
_____

'God, grant me the serenity to accept the things I cannot change'

_____
_____
_____
_____

- ☐ Prayer & meditation
- ☐ Service/help someone
- ☐ Spiritual reading
- ☐ Exercise
- ☐ Call someone
- ☐ ....

'...We consider our plans for the day'

	6 am
	7 am
	8 am
	9 am
	10 am
	11 am
	12 pm
	1 pm
	2 pm
	3 pm
	4 pm
	5 pm
	6 pm
	7 pm
	8 pm
	9 pm

journal

How can I take better care of my body?

_____
_____
_____
_____
_____
_____
_____
_____
_____
_____
_____

personal inventory

'When we retire at night, we constructively review our day'

Did I do something for someone else today?

What did I accomplish today?

What have I done for my recovery today?

Am I taking care of my body?

What could I have done better?

Was I unloving today (cold, unresponsive, indifferent)?

Date: _____ Sobriety Tracker: _____

journal

> Who are the most important people in my life? Why?

_____
_____
_____
_____
_____
_____
_____
_____
_____
_____
_____
_____

personal inventory

'When we retire at night, we constructively review our day'

Was I resentful, selfish, dishonest or afraid?	_____
Do I owe an apology?	_____
Have I kept something to myself which should be discussed with another person at once?	_____
Was I kind and loving towards all?	_____
What could I have done better?	_____
Was I thinking about myself most of the time? Or was I thinking of what I could do for others, of what I could pack into the stream of life?	_____

I'm grateful for...

_____
_____
_____

today I accept...

_____
_____

☐ Prayer & meditation   ☐ Service/help someone

☐ Spiritual reading   ☐ Exercise

☐ Call someone   ☐ ....

'On awakening let us think about the twenty-four hours ahead...'

6 am
7 am
8 am
9 am
10 am
11 am
12 pm
1 pm
2 pm
3 pm
4 pm
5 pm
6 pm
7 pm
8 pm
9 pm

Weekly Check-in

Review of the week

- ☐ Review My vision for the future
- ☐ Review My Rescue Plan
- ☐ Review People to stay in touch with
- ☐ Complete Spiritual Planner

What's been the biggest positive this week?

What fears have been holding me back?

Do I need to ask for some help next week? Is there anyone who needs my help?

Have I been looking after myself this week?

Spiritual Planner

My 2 main spiritual/recovery priorities for this week:

1.

2.

Spiritual and recovery-based activities for the week:

monday

tuesday

wednesday

thursday

friday

saturday

sunday

Date: _____ Sobriety Tracker: _____

journal

What things do I really value in my life?

_____
_____
_____
_____
_____
_____
_____
_____
_____
_____
_____
_____
_____

personal inventory

'When we retire at night, we constructively review our day'

Was I resentful, selfish, dishonest or afraid?
_____
_____

Do I owe an apology?
_____
_____

Have I kept something to myself which should be discussed with another person at once?
_____
_____
_____
_____

Was I kind and loving towards all?
_____
_____

What could I have done better?
_____
_____

Was I thinking about myself most of the time? Or was I thinking of what I could do for others, of what I could pack into the stream of life?
_____
_____
_____
_____
_____

I'm grateful for...

_____
_____
_____

today I accept...

_____
_____
_____

☐ Prayer & meditation   ☐ Service/help someone

☐ Spiritual reading   ☐ Exercise

☐ Call someone   ☐ _____

'On awakening let us think about the twenty-four hours ahead...'

6 am	
7 am	
8 am	
9 am	
10 am	
11 am	
12 pm	
1 pm	
2 pm	
3 pm	
4 pm	
5 pm	
6 pm	
7 pm	
8 pm	
9 pm	

'A genuine gratitude for blessings received'

_____
_____
_____
_____
_____

'God, grant me the serenity to accept the things I cannot change'

_____
_____
_____

- ☐ Prayer & meditation
- ☐ Service/help someone
- ☐ Spiritual reading
- ☐ Exercise
- ☐ Call someone
- ☐ ....

'...We consider our plans for the day'

	6 am
	7 am
	8 am
	9 am
	10 am
	11 am
	12 pm
	1 pm
	2 pm
	3 pm
	4 pm
	5 pm
	6 pm
	7 pm
	8 pm
	9 pm

Date: _____   Sobriety Tracker: _____

journal

> How can I be less judgemental?

_____
_____
_____
_____
_____
_____
_____
_____
_____
_____
_____
_____
_____

personal inventory

'When we retire at night, we constructively review our day'

Was I honest with others and myself today?
_____

What can I celebrate? What could I have done differently?
_____

How was my serenity? Did anything happen that caused me to lose it? What was my part in it?
_____

Am I spending time on myself?
_____

What did I do to connect with my higher power?
_____

Did fear prevent me from doing anything today?
_____

Date: _____   Sobriety Tracker: _____

journal

> How can I avoid being a mental loafer today?

_____
_____
_____
_____
_____
_____
_____
_____
_____
_____
_____
_____

personal inventory

'When we retire at night, we constructively review our day'

Was I resentful, selfish, dishonest or afraid?
_____
_____

Do I owe an apology?
_____
_____

Have I kept something to myself which should be discussed with another person at once?
_____
_____
_____

Was I kind and loving towards all?
_____
_____

What could I have done better?
_____
_____

Was I thinking about myself most of the time? Or was I thinking of what I could do for others, of what I could pack into the stream of life?
_____
_____
_____
_____

I'm grateful for...
_____
_____
_____
_____

today I accept...
_____
_____
_____

- ☐ Prayer & meditation
- ☐ Service/help someone
- ☐ Spiritual reading
- ☐ Exercise
- ☐ Call someone
- ☐ ....

'On awakening let us think about the twenty-four hours ahead...'

6 am	
7 am	
8 am	
9 am	
10 am	
11 am	
12 pm	
1 pm	
2 pm	
3 pm	
4 pm	
5 pm	
6 pm	
7 pm	
8 pm	
9 pm	

'A genuine gratitude for blessings received'

....
....
....
....

'God, grant me the serenity to accept the things I cannot change'

....
....
....
....

- ☐ Prayer & meditation
- ☐ Service/help someone
- ☐ Spiritual reading
- ☐ Exercise
- ☐ Call someone
- ☐ ....

'...We consider our plans for the day'

	6 am
	7 am
	8 am
	9 am
	10 am
	11 am
	12 pm
	1 pm
	2 pm
	3 pm
	4 pm
	5 pm
	6 pm
	7 pm
	8 pm
	9 pm

Date: ....   Sobriety Tracker: ....

journal

How am I spending the majority of my time?

....
....
....
....
....
....
....
....
....
....
....
....
....
....
....

personal inventory

'When we retire at night, we constructively review our day'

Have I practiced any of my character defects?

Am I keeping any secrets?

Was I honest? Did I keep my word with everyone? Did I keep my word with myself?

Am I trying to fill the void with external stimuli?

Did I learn something useful today? Or was I a mental loafer?

Was I concerned today with thoughts or behaviours linked to my addiction?

Date: _____   Sobriety Tracker: _____

journal

What qualities do I wish to develop?

....
....
....
....
....
....
....
....
....
....
....
....
....

personal inventory

'When we retire at night, we constructively review our day'

Was I resentful, selfish, dishonest or afraid?	....
Do I owe an apology?	....
Have I kept something to myself which should be discussed with another person at once?	....
Was I kind and loving towards all?	....
What could I have done better?	....
Was I thinking about myself most of the time? Or was I thinking of what I could do for others, of what I could pack into the stream of life?	....

I'm grateful for...

....
....
....

today I accept...

....
....
....

☐ Prayer & meditation   ☐ Service/help someone

☐ Spiritual reading   ☐ Exercise

☐ Call someone   ☐ ....

'On awakening let us think about the twenty-four hours ahead...'

6 am
7 am
8 am
9 am
10 am
11 am
12 pm
1 pm
2 pm
3 pm
4 pm
5 pm
6 pm
7 pm
8 pm
9 pm

'A genuine gratitude for blessings received'

....

....

'God, grant me the serenity to accept the things I cannot change'

....

....

☐ Prayer & meditation ☐ Service/help someone

☐ Spiritual reading ☐ Exercise

☐ Call someone ☐ ....

'...We consider our plans for the day'

	6 am
	7 am
	8 am
	9 am
	10 am
	11 am
	12 pm
	1 pm
	2 pm
	3 pm
	4 pm
	5 pm
	6 pm
	7 pm
	8 pm
	9 pm

Date: _____   Sobriety Tracker: _____

journal

What can I do or create that brings me inner peace and joy?

....

....

....

....

....

....

....

....

....

....

....

....

personal inventory

'When we retire at night, we constructively review our day'

How did I take care of my health (physical, emotional, spiritual) today?

What have I enjoyed about today?

How did I show love to others? Did I act unlovingly towards anyone?

Who neds my prayers today?

Am I holding any resentments?

How is my spiritual condition?

Date: _____   Sobriety Tracker: _____

journal

> What small changes to my lifestyle can I make that would positively impact the world?

_____
_____
_____
_____
_____
_____
_____
_____
_____
_____
_____
_____

personal inventory

'When we retire at night, we constructively review our day'

Was I resentful, selfish, dishonest or afraid?	_____
Do I owe an apology?	_____
Have I kept something to myself which should be discussed with another person at once?	_____
Was I kind and loving towards all?	_____
What could I have done better?	_____
Was I thinking about myself most of the time? Or was I thinking of what I could do for others, of what I could pack into the stream of life?	_____

I'm grateful for...

....
....
....
....

today I accept...

....
....

- [ ] Prayer & meditation
- [ ] Service/help someone
- [ ] Spiritual reading
- [ ] Exercise
- [ ] Call someone
- [ ] ....

'On awakening let us think about the twenty-four hours ahead...'

6 am
7 am
8 am
9 am
10 am
11 am
12 pm
1 pm
2 pm
3 pm
4 pm
5 pm
6 pm
7 pm
8 pm
9 pm

Weekly Check-in

Review of the week

- [ ] Review How I'll know if I'm heading for a relapse
- [ ] Review My Character Defects
- [ ] Review People to stay in touch with
- [ ] Complete Spiritual Planner

What's gone well this week?

What are the biggest distractions in my life? How can I remove them?

Which part of the program do I need to prioritise next week?

How is my spiritual condition?

Spiritual Planner

My 2 main spiritual/recovery priorities for this week:

1.

2.

Spiritual and recovery-based activities for the week:

monday

tuesday

wednesday

thursday

friday

saturday

sunday

Date: _____ Sobriety Tracker: _____

journal

How often do I procrastinate?

_____
_____
_____
_____
_____
_____
_____
_____
_____
_____
_____
_____
_____

personal inventory

'When we retire at night, we constructively review our day'

Was I resentful, selfish, dishonest or afraid?
_____

Do I owe an apology?
_____

Have I kept something to myself which should be discussed with another person at once?
_____

Was I kind and loving towards all?
_____

What could I have done better?
_____

Was I thinking about myself most of the time? Or was I thinking of what I could do for others, of what I could pack into the stream of life?
_____

I'm grateful for...

_____
_____
_____

today I accept...

_____
_____

☐ Prayer & meditation   ☐ Service/help someone

☐ Spiritual reading   ☐ Exercise

☐ Call someone   ☐ ....

'On awakening let us think about the twenty-four hours ahead...'

6 am
7 am
8 am
9 am
10 am
11 am
12 pm
1 pm
2 pm
3 pm
4 pm
5 pm
6 pm
7 pm
8 pm
9 pm

'A genuine gratitude for blessings received'

....

....

....

....

'God, grant me the serenity to accept the things I cannot change'

....

....

....

....

☐ Prayer & meditation   ☐ Service/help someone

☐ Spiritual reading   ☐ Exercise

☐ Call someone   ☐ ....

'...We consider our plans for the day'

6 am

7 am

8 am

9 am

10 am

11 am

12 pm

1 pm

2 pm

3 pm

4 pm

5 pm

6 pm

7 pm

8 pm

9 pm

journal

What's on my 'to-do' list that never gets done?

....

....

....

....

....

....

....

....

....

....

....

....

....

....

personal inventory

'When we retire at night, we constructively review our day'

Was I unkind (cruel, harsh, unfeeling)?

Who did I help today?

How did I show love to myself? Did I talk negatively to myself?

Am I obsessing about anything?

What am I proud of today?

Was I patient, kind and compassionate? What caused me to lose these attitudes? Do I owe anyone amends?

journal

When's the last time I learned something new?

I'm grateful for...

today I accept...

- ☐ Prayer & meditation
- ☐ Service/help someone
- ☐ Spiritual reading
- ☐ Exercise
- ☐ Call someone
- ☐

'On awakening let us think about the twenty-four hours ahead...'

6 am

7 am

8 am

9 am

10 am

11 am

12 pm

1 pm

2 pm

3 pm

4 pm

5 pm

6 pm

7 pm

8 pm

9 pm

personal inventory

'When we retire at night, we constructively review our day'

Was I resentful, selfish, dishonest or afraid?

Do I owe an apology?

Have I kept something to myself which should be discussed with another person at once?

Was I kind and loving towards all?

What could I have done better?

Was I thinking about myself most of the time? Or was I thinking of what I could do for others, of what I could pack into the stream of life?

'A genuine gratitude for blessings received'

....
....
....
....
....

'God, grant me the serenity to accept the things I cannot change'

....
....
....
....
....

☐ Prayer & meditation   ☐ Service/help someone

☐ Spiritual reading   ☐ Exercise

☐ Call someone   ☐ ....

'...We consider our plans for the day'

	6 am
	7 am
	8 am
	9 am
	10 am
	11 am
	12 pm
	1 pm
	2 pm
	3 pm
	4 pm
	5 pm
	6 pm
	7 pm
	8 pm
	9 pm

Date: _____   Sobriety Tracker: _____

journal

Do I have a relationship that needs mending?

....
....
....
....
....
....
....
....
....
....
....
....
....
....

personal inventory

'When we retire at night, we constructively review our day'

Did I do something for someone else today?

What did I accomplish today?

What have I done for my recovery today?

Am I taking care of my body?

What could I have done better?

Was I unloving today (cold, unresponsive, indifferent)?

Date: _____   Sobriety Tracker: _____

journal

> What is no longer acceptable in my life?

_____
_____
_____
_____
_____
_____
_____
_____
_____
_____
_____
_____

personal inventory

'When we retire at night, we constructively review our day'

Was I resentful, selfish, dishonest or afraid?
_____
_____

Do I owe an apology?
_____
_____

Have I kept something to myself which should be discussed with another person at once?
_____
_____
_____
_____

Was I kind and loving towards all?
_____
_____

What could I have done better?
_____
_____

Was I thinking about myself most of the time? Or was I thinking of what I could do for others, of what I could pack into the stream of life?
_____
_____
_____
_____

I'm grateful for...

_____
_____
_____

today I accept...

_____
_____

☐ Prayer & meditation   ☐ Service/help someone

☐ Spiritual reading   ☐ Exercise

☐ Call someone   ☐ _____

'On awakening let us think about the twenty-four hours ahead...'

6 am
7 am
8 am
9 am
10 am
11 am
12 pm
1 pm
2 pm
3 pm
4 pm
5 pm
6 pm
7 pm
8 pm
9 pm

....
....
....
....

....
....
....

- [ ] Prayer & meditation
- [ ] Service/help someone
- [ ] Spiritual reading
- [ ] Exercise
- [ ] Call someone
- [ ] ....

	6 am
	7 am
	8 am
	9 am
	10 am
	11 am
	12 pm
	1 pm
	2 pm
	3 pm
	4 pm
	5 pm
	6 pm
	7 pm
	8 pm
	9 pm

Date: _____   Sobriety Tracker: _____

journal

Do I enjoy spending time alone?

....
....
....
....
....
....
....
....
....
....
....
....
....
....

personal inventory

Was I honest with others and myself today?

What can I celebrate? What could I have done differently?

How was my serenity? Did anything happen that caused me to lose it? What was my part in it?

Am I spending time on myself?

What did I do to connect with my higher power?

Did fear prevent me from doing anything today?

Date: _____   Sobriety Tracker: _____

journal

> What stresses me out?

_____
_____
_____
_____
_____
_____
_____
_____
_____
_____
_____
_____
_____

personal inventory

'When we retire at night, we constructively review our day'

Was I resentful, selfish, dishonest or afraid?
_____

Do I owe an apology?
_____

Have I kept something to myself which should be discussed with another person at once?
_____

Was I kind and loving towards all?
_____

What could I have done better?
_____

Was I thinking about myself most of the time? Or was I thinking of what I could do for others, of what I could pack into the stream of life?
_____

I'm grateful for...

_____
_____
_____

today I accept...

_____
_____

- ☐ Prayer & meditation
- ☐ Service/help someone
- ☐ Spiritual reading
- ☐ Exercise
- ☐ Call someone
- ☐ _____

'On awakening let us think about the twenty-four hours ahead...'

6 am	
7 am	
8 am	
9 am	
10 am	
11 am	
12 pm	
1 pm	
2 pm	
3 pm	
4 pm	
5 pm	
6 pm	
7 pm	
8 pm	
9 pm	

Weekly Check-in

Review of the week

- [ ] Review My Rock Bottom
- [ ] Review My Character Defects
- [ ] Review People to stay in touch with
- [ ] Complete Spiritual Planner

What have I achieved this week?

What's not working? What am I willing to do about it?

What one thing can I do next week that will have the biggest positive impact on my life?

What do I need to make a decision about?

Spiritual Planner

My 2 main spiritual/recovery priorities for this week:

1.

2.

Spiritual and recovery-based activities for the week:

monday

tuesday

wednesday

thursday

friday

saturday

sunday

Date: _____ Sobriety Tracker: _____

journal

How do I currently feel about myself?

_____
_____
_____
_____
_____
_____
_____
_____
_____
_____
_____
_____
_____
_____
_____

I'm grateful for...

_____
_____
_____
_____

today I accept...

_____
_____
_____
_____

- [ ] Prayer & meditation
- [ ] Service/help someone
- [ ] Spiritual reading
- [ ] Exercise
- [ ] Call someone
- [ ] ....

'On awakening let us think about the twenty-four hours ahead...'

6 am	
7 am	
8 am	
9 am	
10 am	
11 am	
12 pm	
1 pm	
2 pm	
3 pm	
4 pm	
5 pm	
6 pm	
7 pm	
8 pm	
9 pm	

personal inventory

'When we retire at night, we constructively review our day'

Was I resentful, selfish, dishonest or afraid?
_____

Do I owe an apology?
_____

Have I kept something to myself which should be discussed with another person at once?
_____

Was I kind and loving towards all?
_____

What could I have done better?
_____

Was I thinking about myself most of the time? Or was I thinking of what I could do for others, of what I could pack into the stream of life?
_____

'A genuine gratitude for blessings received'

'God, grant me the serenity to accept the things I cannot change'

☐ Prayer & meditation   ☐ Service/help someone

☐ Spiritual reading   ☐ Exercise

☐ Call someone   ☐ ....

'...We consider our plans for the day'

6 am

7 am

8 am

9 am

10 am

11 am

12 pm

1 pm

2 pm

3 pm

4 pm

5 pm

6 pm

7 pm

8 pm

9 pm

journal

What do I need to let go of?

personal inventory

'When we retire at night, we constructively review our day'

Have I practiced any of my character defects?

Am I keeping any secrets?

Was I honest? Did I keep my word with everyone? Did I keep my word with myself?

Am I trying to fill the void with external stimuli?

Did I learn something useful today? Or was I a mental loafer?

Was I concerned today with thoughts or behaviours linked to my addiction?

Date: _____   Sobriety Tracker: _____

journal

> What decisions do I need to make that I've been putting off?

....
....
....
....
....
....
....
....
....
....
....
....
....
....

personal inventory

'When we retire at night, we constructively review our day'

Was I resentful, selfish, dishonest or afraid?	....
Do I owe an apology?	....
Have I kept something to myself which should be discussed with another person at once?	....
Was I kind and loving towards all?	....
What could I have done better?	....
Was I thinking about myself most of the time? Or was I thinking of what I could do for others, of what I could pack into the stream of life?	....

I'm grateful for...

....
....
....
....

today I accept...

....
....

☐ Prayer & meditation   ☐ Service/help someone

☐ Spiritual reading   ☐ Exercise

☐ Call someone   ☐ ....

'On awakening let us think about the twenty-four hours ahead...'

6 am	
7 am	
8 am	
9 am	
10 am	
11 am	
12 pm	
1 pm	
2 pm	
3 pm	
4 pm	
5 pm	
6 pm	
7 pm	
8 pm	
9 pm	

'A genuine gratitude for blessings received'

....
....
....
....

'God, grant me the serenity to accept the things I cannot change'

....
....
....

- ☐ Prayer & meditation
- ☐ Service/help someone
- ☐ Spiritual reading
- ☐ Exercise
- ☐ Call someone
- ☐ ....

'...We consider our plans for the day'

	6 am
	7 am
	8 am
	9 am
	10 am
	11 am
	12 pm
	1 pm
	2 pm
	3 pm
	4 pm
	5 pm
	6 pm
	7 pm
	8 pm
	9 pm

Date: _____   Sobriety Tracker: _____

journal

Do I need to be more open-minded and accepting?

....
....
....
....
....
....
....
....
....
....
....
....
....
....

personal inventory

'When we retire at night, we constructively review our day'

How did I take care of my health (physical, emotional, spiritual) today?

What have I enjoyed about today?

How did I show love to others? Did I act unlovingly towards anyone?

Who neds my prayers today?

Am I holding any resentments?

How is my spiritual condition?

Date: _____   Sobriety Tracker: _____

journal

Do I have healthy fun, or is it destructive?

_____
_____
_____
_____
_____
_____
_____
_____
_____
_____
_____
_____

personal inventory

'When we retire at night, we constructively review our day'

Was I resentful, selfish, dishonest or afraid?

Do I owe an apology?

Have I kept something to myself which should be discussed with another person at once?

Was I kind and loving towards all?

What could I have done better?

Was I thinking about myself most of the time? Or was I thinking of what I could do for others, of what I could pack into the stream of life?

I'm grateful for...

_____
_____
_____

today I accept...

_____
_____

☐ Prayer & meditation   ☐ Service/help someone

☐ Spiritual reading   ☐ Exercise

☐ Call someone   ☐ ....

'On awakening let us think about the twenty-four hours ahead...'

6 am
7 am
8 am
9 am
10 am
11 am
12 pm
1 pm
2 pm
3 pm
4 pm
5 pm
6 pm
7 pm
8 pm
9 pm

'A genuine gratitude for blessings received'

....

....

....

....

'God, grant me the serenity to accept the things I cannot change'

....

....

....

....

- ☐ Prayer & meditation
- ☐ Service/help someone
- ☐ Spiritual reading
- ☐ Exercise
- ☐ Call someone
- ☐ ....

'...We consider our plans for the day'

	6 am
	7 am
	8 am
	9 am
	10 am
	11 am
	12 pm
	1 pm
	2 pm
	3 pm
	4 pm
	5 pm
	6 pm
	7 pm
	8 pm
	9 pm

Date: ....   Sobriety Tracker: ....

journal

> Where is my favourite place to be? Why?

....

....

....

....

....

....

....

....

....

....

....

....

....

....

....

personal inventory

'When we retire at night, we constructively review our day'

Was I unkind (cruel, harsh, unfeeling)?

Who did I help today?

How did I show love to myself? Did I talk negatively to myself?

Am I obsessing about anything?

What am I proud of today?

Was I patient, kind and compassionate? What caused me to lose these attitudes? Do I owe anyone amends?

journal

When did I last make a new friend?

_____

_____

_____

_____

_____

_____

_____

_____

_____

_____

_____

_____

_____

personal inventory

'When we retire at night, we constructively review our day'

Was I resentful, selfish, dishonest or afraid?

Do I owe an apology?

Have I kept something to myself which should be discussed with another person at once?

Was I kind and loving towards all?

What could I have done better?

Was I thinking about myself most of the time? Or was I thinking of what I could do for others, of what I could pack into the stream of life?

I'm grateful for...

_____

_____

_____

today I accept...

_____

_____

_____

☐ Prayer & meditation   ☐ Service/help someone

☐ Spiritual reading   ☐ Exercise

☐ Call someone   ☐ ....

'On awakening let us think about the twenty-four hours ahead...'

6 am
7 am
8 am
9 am
10 am
11 am
12 pm
1 pm
2 pm
3 pm
4 pm
5 pm
6 pm
7 pm
8 pm
9 pm

Weekly Check-in

Review of the week

- ☐ Review My Triggers
- ☐ Review My Rescue Plan
- ☐ Review People to stay in touch with
- ☐ Complete Spiritual Planner

What's working and why is it working?

What part of my recovery have I been neglecting?

What do I need to pay more attention to?

Have I had fun this week? How can I have more fun?

Spiritual Planner

My 2 main spiritual/recovery priorities for this week:

1.

2.

Spiritual and recovery-based activities for the week:

monday

tuesday

wednesday

thursday

friday

saturday

sunday

Date: _____   Sobriety Tracker: _____

journal

> How can I be a better father/mother/sister/brother/son/daughter?

_____
_____
_____
_____
_____
_____
_____
_____
_____
_____
_____
_____
_____

I'm grateful for...

_____
_____
_____

today I accept...

_____
_____
_____

☐ Prayer & meditation   ☐ Service/help someone

☐ Spiritual reading   ☐ Exercise

☐ Call someone   ☐ _____

'On awakening let us think about the twenty-four hours ahead...'

| 6 am |
| 7 am |
| 8 am |
| 9 am |
| 10 am |
| 11 am |
| 12 pm |
| 1 pm |
| 2 pm |
| 3 pm |
| 4 pm |
| 5 pm |
| 6 pm |
| 7 pm |
| 8 pm |
| 9 pm |

personal inventory

'When we retire at night, we constructively review our day'

Was I resentful, selfish, dishonest or afraid?
_____

Do I owe an apology?
_____

Have I kept something to myself which should be discussed with another person at once?
_____

Was I kind and loving towards all?
_____

What could I have done better?
_____

Was I thinking about myself most of the time? Or was I thinking of what I could do for others, of what I could pack into the stream of life?
_____

A genuine gratitude for blessings received'

....
....
....
....

'God, grant me the serenity to accept the things I cannot change'

....
....
....

☐ Prayer & meditation

☐ Service/help someone

☐ Spiritual reading

☐ Exercise

☐ Call someone

☐ ....

'...We consider our plans for the day'

6 am

7 am

8 am

9 am

10 am

11 am

12 pm

1 pm

2 pm

3 pm

4 pm

5 pm

6 pm

7 pm

8 pm

9 pm

journal

What makes me tired?
What gives me energy?

personal inventory

'When we retire at night, we constructively review our day'

Did I do something for someone else today?

What did I accomplish today?

What have I done for my recovery today?

Am I taking care of my body?

What could I have done better?

Was I unloving today (cold, unresponsive, indifferent)?

Date: _____ Sobriety Tracker: _____

journal

What makes me happy?

....
....
....
....
....
....
....
....
....
....
....
....
....
....
....

personal inventory

'When we retire at night, we constructively review our day'

Was I resentful, selfish, dishonest or afraid?
....

Do I owe an apology?
....

Have I kept something to myself which should be discussed with another person at once?
....

Was I kind and loving towards all?
....

What could I have done better?
....

Was I thinking about myself most of the time? Or was I thinking of what I could do for others, of what I could pack into the stream of life?
....

I'm grateful for...

....
....
....

today I accept...

....
....

☐ Prayer & meditation   ☐ Service/help someone

☐ Spiritual reading   ☐ Exercise

☐ Call someone   ☐ ....

'On awakening let us think about the twenty-four hours ahead...'

6 am	
7 am	
8 am	
9 am	
10 am	
11 am	
12 pm	
1 pm	
2 pm	
3 pm	
4 pm	
5 pm	
6 pm	
7 pm	
8 pm	
9 pm	

A genuine gratitude for blessings received'

....
....
....
....

'God, grant me the serenity to accept the things I cannot change'

....
....
....
....

journal

How can I deepen my relationship with my higher power?

....
....
....
....
....
....
....
....
....
....
....
....
....
....
....

☐ Prayer & meditation   ☐ Service/help someone

☐ Spiritual reading   ☐ Exercise

☐ Call someone   ☐ ....

...We consider our plans for the day'

	6 am
	7 am
	8 am
	9 am
	10 am
	11 am
	12 pm
	1 pm
	2 pm
	3 pm
	4 pm
	5 pm
	6 pm
	7 pm
	8 pm
	9 pm

personal inventory

'When we retire at night, we constructively review our day'

Was I honest with others and myself today?
....
....

What can I celebrate? What could I have done differently?
....
....
....

How was my serenity? Did anything happen that caused me to lose it? What was my part in it?
....
....
....
....
....

Am I spending time on myself?
....
....

What did I do to connect with my higher power?
....
....
....

Did fear prevent me from doing anything today?
....
....

Date: _____ Sobriety Tracker: _____

journal

Am I good at handling change?
How does it make me feel?

_____
_____
_____
_____
_____
_____
_____
_____
_____
_____
_____
_____

personal inventory

'When we retire at night, we constructively review our day'

Was I resentful, selfish, dishonest or afraid?
_____

Do I owe an apology?
_____

Have I kept something to myself which should be discussed with another person at once?
_____
_____
_____

Was I kind and loving towards all?
_____
_____

What could I have done better?
_____
_____

Was I thinking about myself most of the time? Or was I thinking of what I could do for others, of what I could pack into the stream of life?
_____
_____
_____
_____
_____

I'm grateful for...

_____
_____
_____

today I accept...

_____
_____
_____

☐ Prayer & meditation   ☐ Service/help someone

☐ Spiritual reading   ☐ Exercise

☐ Call someone   ☐ ....

'On awakening let us think about the twenty-four hours ahead...'

6 am
7 am
8 am
9 am
10 am
11 am
12 pm
1 pm
2 pm
3 pm
4 pm
5 pm
6 pm
7 pm
8 pm
9 pm

'A genuine gratitude for blessings received'

....
....
....
....

'God, grant me the serenity to accept the things I cannot change'

....
....
....

☐ Prayer & meditation   ☐ Service/help someone

☐ Spiritual reading   ☐ Exercise

☐ Call someone   ☐ ....

'...We consider our plans for the day'

6 am	
7 am	
8 am	
9 am	
10 am	
11 am	
12 pm	
1 pm	
2 pm	
3 pm	
4 pm	
5 pm	
6 pm	
7 pm	
8 pm	
9 pm	

journal

Do I need to listen more to those in my life?

....
....
....
....
....
....
....
....
....
....
....
....
....
....
....
....
....

personal inventory

'When we retire at night, we constructively review our day'

Have I practiced any of my character defects?	
Am I keeping any secrets?	
Was I honest? Did I keep my word with everyone? Did I keep my word with myself?	
Am I trying to fill the void with external stimuli?	
Did I learn something useful today? Or was I a mental loafer?	
Was I concerned today with thoughts or behaviours linked to my addiction?	

Date: _____ Sobriety Tracker: _____

journal

> What's one of the most important things I learnt from my parents?

_____
_____
_____
_____
_____
_____
_____
_____
_____
_____
_____
_____

personal inventory

'When we retire at night, we constructively review our day'

Was I resentful, selfish, dishonest or afraid?
_____

Do I owe an apology?
_____

Have I kept something to myself which should be discussed with another person at once?
_____
_____

Was I kind and loving towards all?
_____

What could I have done better?
_____

Was I thinking about myself most of the time? Or was I thinking of what I could do for others, of what I could pack into the stream of life?
_____
_____
_____

I'm grateful for...

_____
_____
_____

today I accept...

_____
_____

☐ Prayer & meditation   ☐ Service/help someone

☐ Spiritual reading   ☐ Exercise

☐ Call someone   ☐ _____

'On awakening let us think about the twenty-four hours ahead...'

6 am	
7 am	
8 am	
9 am	
10 am	
11 am	
12 pm	
1 pm	
2 pm	
3 pm	
4 pm	
5 pm	
6 pm	
7 pm	
8 pm	
9 pm	

Weekly Check-in

Review of the week

- [ ] Review What would happen if I relapse

- [ ] Review My Character Defects

- [ ] Review People to stay in touch with

- [ ] Complete Spiritual Planner

What's made me happy this week?

What's been most difficult this week? Do I need to change something?

What do I need to start doing? What do I need to stop doing?

How can I prioritise my time better?

Spiritual Planner

My 2 main spiritual/recovery priorities for this week:

1.

2.

Spiritual and recovery-based activities for the week:

monday

tuesday

wednesday

thursday

friday

saturday

sunday

Date: _____ Sobriety Tracker: _____

journal

> Am I engaging in activities to escape reality?

_____
_____
_____
_____
_____
_____
_____
_____
_____
_____
_____
_____
_____
_____
_____

personal inventory

'When we retire at night, we constructively review our day'

Was I resentful, selfish, dishonest or afraid?
_____

Do I owe an apology?
_____

Have I kept something to myself which should be discussed with another person at once?
_____

Was I kind and loving towards all?
_____

What could I have done better?
_____

Was I thinking about myself most of the time? Or was I thinking of what I could do for others, of what I could pack into the stream of life?
_____

I'm grateful for...

_____
_____
_____
_____

today I accept...

_____
_____
_____

☐ Prayer & meditation   ☐ Service/help someone

☐ Spiritual reading   ☐ Exercise

☐ Call someone   ☐ _____

'On awakening let us think about the twenty-four hours ahead...'

6 am	
7 am	
8 am	
9 am	
10 am	
11 am	
12 pm	
1 pm	
2 pm	
3 pm	
4 pm	
5 pm	
6 pm	
7 pm	
8 pm	
9 pm	

'A genuine gratitude for blessings received'

....

....

....

'God, grant me the serenity to accept the things I cannot change'

....

....

....

- ☐ Prayer & meditation
- ☐ Service/help someone
- ☐ Spiritual reading
- ☐ Exercise
- ☐ Call someone
- ☐ ....

'...We consider our plans for the day'

	6 am
	7 am
	8 am
	9 am
	10 am
	11 am
	12 pm
	1 pm
	2 pm
	3 pm
	4 pm
	5 pm
	6 pm
	7 pm
	8 pm
	9 pm

journal

What scares me?

....

....

....

....

....

....

....

....

....

....

....

....

....

personal inventory

'When we retire at night, we constructively review our day'

How did I take care of my health (physical, emotional, spiritual) today?

What have I enjoyed about today?

How did I show love to others? Did I act unlovingly towards anyone?

Who neds my prayers today?

Am I holding any resentments?

How is my spiritual condition?

journal

Who needs my love today?
Who needs my prayers?

_____
_____
_____
_____
_____
_____
_____
_____
_____
_____
_____
_____
_____
_____

personal inventory

'When we retire at night, we constructively review our day'

Was I resentful, selfish, dishonest or afraid?

Do I owe an apology?

Have I kept something to myself which should be discussed with another person at once?

Was I kind and loving towards all?

What could I have done better?

Was I thinking about myself most of the time? Or was I thinking of what I could do for others, of what I could pack into the stream of life?

I'm grateful for...

_____
_____
_____

today I accept...

_____
_____

☐ Prayer & meditation   ☐ Service/help someone

☐ Spiritual reading   ☐ Exercise

☐ Call someone   ☐ ....

'On awakening let us think about the twenty-four hours ahead...'

6 am
7 am
8 am
9 am
10 am
11 am
12 pm
1 pm
2 pm
3 pm
4 pm
5 pm
6 pm
7 pm
8 pm
9 pm

'A genuine gratitude for blessings received'

_____
_____
_____
_____

'God, grant me the serenity to accept the things I cannot change'

_____
_____
_____

☐ Prayer & meditation   ☐ Service/help someone

☐ Spiritual reading   ☐ Exercise

☐ Call someone   ☐ ....

'...We consider our plans for the day'

	6 am
	7 am
	8 am
	9 am
	10 am
	11 am
	12 pm
	1 pm
	2 pm
	3 pm
	4 pm
	5 pm
	6 pm
	7 pm
	8 pm
	9 pm

journal

What makes me sad?

_____
_____
_____
_____
_____
_____
_____
_____
_____
_____
_____
_____
_____
_____

personal inventory

'When we retire at night, we constructively review our day'

Was I unkind (cruel, harsh, unfeeling)?

Who did I help today?

How did I show love to myself? Did I talk negatively to myself?

Am I obsessing about anything?

What am I proud of today?

Was I patient, kind and compassionate? What caused me to lose these attitudes? Do I owe anyone amends?

journal

What would I tell my younger self if I could?

_____
_____
_____
_____
_____
_____
_____
_____
_____
_____
_____
_____
_____
_____

personal inventory

'When we retire at night, we constructively review our day'

Was I resentful, selfish, dishonest or afraid?
_____

Do I owe an apology?
_____

Have I kept something to myself which should be discussed with another person at once?
_____
_____
_____

Was I kind and loving towards all?
_____

What could I have done better?
_____

Was I thinking about myself most of the time? Or was I thinking of what I could do for others, of what I could pack into the stream of life?
_____
_____
_____

I'm grateful for...

_____
_____
_____
_____

today I accept...

_____
_____
_____

☐ Prayer & meditation   ☐ Service/help someone

☐ Spiritual reading   ☐ Exercise

☐ Call someone   ☐ _____

'On awakening let us think about the twenty-four hours ahead...'

6 am
7 am
8 am
9 am
10 am
11 am
12 pm
1 pm
2 pm
3 pm
4 pm
5 pm
6 pm
7 pm
8 pm
9 pm

'A genuine gratitude for blessings received'

_____
_____
_____
_____
_____

'God, grant me the serenity to accept the things I cannot change'

_____
_____
_____
_____

- ☐ Prayer & meditation
- ☐ Service/help someone
- ☐ Spiritual reading
- ☐ Exercise
- ☐ Call someone
- ☐ ....

'...We consider our plans for the day'

	6 am
	7 am
	8 am
	9 am
	10 am
	11 am
	12 pm
	1 pm
	2 pm
	3 pm
	4 pm
	5 pm
	6 pm
	7 pm
	8 pm
	9 pm

Date: _____   Sobriety Tracker: _____

journal

What's my biggest weakness?

_____
_____
_____
_____
_____
_____
_____
_____
_____
_____
_____
_____
_____

personal inventory

'When we retire at night, we constructively review our day'

Did I do something for someone else today?
_____

What did I accomplish today?
_____

What have I done for my recovery today?
_____

Am I taking care of my body?
_____

What could I have done better?
_____

Was I unloving today (cold, unresponsive, indifferent)?
_____

Date: _____ Sobriety Tracker: _____

journal

> What can I do to improve my relationship with my family?

_____
_____
_____
_____
_____
_____
_____
_____
_____
_____
_____
_____
_____
_____
_____

personal inventory

'When we retire at night, we constructively review our day'

Was I resentful, selfish, dishonest or afraid?	_____
Do I owe an apology?	_____
Have I kept something to myself which should be discussed with another person at once?	_____
Was I kind and loving towards all?	_____
What could I have done better?	_____
Was I thinking about myself most of the time? Or was I thinking of what I could do for others, of what I could pack into the stream of life?	_____

I'm grateful for...

_____
_____
_____
_____

today I accept...

_____
_____

☐ Prayer & meditation   ☐ Service/help someone

☐ Spiritual reading   ☐ Exercise

☐ Call someone   ☐ ....

'On awakening let us think about the twenty-four hours ahead...'

6 am
7 am
8 am
9 am
10 am
11 am
12 pm
1 pm
2 pm
3 pm
4 pm
5 pm
6 pm
7 pm
8 pm
9 pm

Weekly Check-in

Review of the week

- [ ] Review My vision for the future
- [ ] Review My Rescue Plan
- [ ] Review People to stay in touch with
- [ ] Complete Spiritual Planner

What's been the biggest positive this week?

What fears have been holding me back?

Do I need to ask for some help next week? Is there anyone who needs my help?

Have I been looking after myself this week?

Spiritual Planner

My 2 main spiritual/recovery priorities for this week:

1.

2.

Spiritual and recovery-based activities for the week:

monday

tuesday

wednesday

thursday

friday

saturday

sunday

Date: _____ Sobriety Tracker: _____

journal

What relaxes me?

_____
_____
_____
_____
_____
_____
_____
_____
_____
_____
_____
_____
_____

personal inventory

'When we retire at night, we constructively review our day'

Was I resentful, selfish, dishonest or afraid?
_____

Do I owe an apology?
_____

Have I kept something to myself which should be discussed with another person at once?
_____

Was I kind and loving towards all?
_____

What could I have done better?
_____

Was I thinking about myself most of the time? Or was I thinking of what I could do for others, of what I could pack into the stream of life?
_____

I'm grateful for...

_____
_____
_____

today I accept...

_____
_____

☐ Prayer & meditation   ☐ Service/help someone

☐ Spiritual reading   ☐ Exercise

☐ Call someone   ☐ ....

'On awakening let us think about the twenty-four hours ahead...'

6 am
7 am
8 am
9 am
10 am
11 am
12 pm
1 pm
2 pm
3 pm
4 pm
5 pm
6 pm
7 pm
8 pm
9 pm

'A genuine gratitude for blessings received'

....
....
....
....

'God, grant me the serenity to accept the
things I cannot change'

....
....
....
....

☐ Prayer &
  meditation

☐ Service/help
  someone

☐ Spiritual
  reading

☐ Exercise

☐ Call someone

☐ ....

'...We consider our plans for the day'

	6 am
	7 am
	8 am
	9 am
	10 am
	11 am
	12 pm
	1 pm
	2 pm
	3 pm
	4 pm
	5 pm
	6 pm
	7 pm
	8 pm
	9 pm

journal

What makes me angry?

....
....
....
....
....
....
....
....
....
....
....

personal inventory

'When we retire at night, we
constructively review our day'

Was I honest with others and myself today?

What can I celebrate? What could I have done differently?

How was my serenity? Did anything happen that caused me to lose it? What was my part in it?

Am I spending time on myself?

What did I do to connect with my higher power?

Did fear prevent me from doing anything today?

Date: _____   Sobriety Tracker: _____

journal

I create the best results in my life when...

....
....
....
....
....
....
....
....
....
....
....
....
....

personal inventory

'When we retire at night, we constructively review our day'

Was I resentful, selfish, dishonest or afraid?
....
....

Do I owe an apology?
....
....

Have I kept something to myself which should be discussed with another person at once?
....
....
....
....

Was I kind and loving towards all?
....
....

What could I have done better?
....
....

Was I thinking about myself most of the time? Or was I thinking of what I could do for others, of what I could pack into the stream of life?
....
....
....
....
....

I'm grateful for...

....
....
....
....

today I accept...

....
....
....

☐ Prayer & meditation   ☐ Service/help someone

☐ Spiritual reading   ☐ Exercise

☐ Call someone   ☐ ....

'On awakening let us think about the twenty-four hours ahead...'

6 am
7 am
8 am
9 am
10 am
11 am
12 pm
1 pm
2 pm
3 pm
4 pm
5 pm
6 pm
7 pm
8 pm
9 pm

'A genuine gratitude for blessings received'

_____
_____
_____
_____

'God, grant me the serenity to accept the things I cannot change'

_____
_____
_____
_____

- ☐ Prayer & meditation
- ☐ Service/help someone
- ☐ Spiritual reading
- ☐ Exercise
- ☐ Call someone
- ☐ ....

'...We consider our plans for the day'

	6 am
	7 am
	8 am
	9 am
	10 am
	11 am
	12 pm
	1 pm
	2 pm
	3 pm
	4 pm
	5 pm
	6 pm
	7 pm
	8 pm
	9 pm

journal

> What is the most important thing in my life?

_____
_____
_____
_____
_____
_____
_____
_____
_____
_____
_____
_____
_____
_____

personal inventory

'When we retire at night, we constructively review our day'

Have I practiced any of my character defects?

Am I keeping any secrets?

Was I honest? Did I keep my word with everyone? Did I keep my word with myself?

Am I trying to fill the void with external stimuli?

Did I learn something useful today? Or was I a mental loafer?

Was I concerned today with thoughts or behaviours linked to my addiction?

journal

Is there anyone I need to forgive?

I'm grateful for...

today I accept...

- ☐ Prayer & meditation
- ☐ Service/help someone
- ☐ Spiritual reading
- ☐ Exercise
- ☐ Call someone
- ☐ ....

'On awakening let us think about the twenty-four hours ahead...'

6 am	
7 am	
8 am	
9 am	
10 am	
11 am	
12 pm	
1 pm	
2 pm	
3 pm	
4 pm	
5 pm	
6 pm	
7 pm	
8 pm	
9 pm	

personal inventory

'When we retire at night, we constructively review our day'

Was I resentful, selfish, dishonest or afraid?

Do I owe an apology?

Have I kept something to myself which should be discussed with another person at once?

Was I kind and loving towards all?

What could I have done better?

Was I thinking about myself most of the time? Or was I thinking of what I could do for others, of what I could pack into the stream of life?

'A genuine gratitude for blessings received'

....
....
....
....

'God, grant me the serenity to accept the things I cannot change'

....
....
....

☐ Prayer & meditation   ☐ Service/help someone

☐ Spiritual reading   ☐ Exercise

☐ Call someone   ☐ ....

'...We consider our plans for the day'

	6 am
	7 am
	8 am
	9 am
	10 am
	11 am
	12 pm
	1 pm
	2 pm
	3 pm
	4 pm
	5 pm
	6 pm
	7 pm
	8 pm
	9 pm

journal

Am I generally positive or negative?

personal inventory

'When we retire at night, we constructively review our day'

How did I take care of my health (physical, emotional, spiritual) today?

What have I enjoyed about today?

How did I show love to others? Did I act unlovingly towards anyone?

Who neds my prayers today?

Am I holding any resentments?

How is my spiritual condition?

Date: _____ Sobriety Tracker: _____

journal

> What or who inspires me?

_____
_____
_____
_____
_____
_____
_____
_____
_____
_____
_____
_____

personal inventory

'When we retire at night, we constructively review our day'

Was I resentful, selfish, dishonest or afraid?
_____
_____

Do I owe an apology?
_____
_____

Have I kept something to myself which should be discussed with another person at once?
_____
_____
_____

Was I kind and loving towards all?
_____
_____

What could I have done better?
_____
_____

Was I thinking about myself most of the time? Or was I thinking of what I could do for others, of what I could pack into the stream of life?
_____
_____
_____
_____

I'm grateful for...

_____
_____
_____

today I accept...

_____
_____

- ☐ Prayer & meditation
- ☐ Service/help someone
- ☐ Spiritual reading
- ☐ Exercise
- ☐ Call someone
- ☐ _____

'On awakening let us think about the twenty-four hours ahead...'

6 am	
7 am	
8 am	
9 am	
10 am	
11 am	
12 pm	
1 pm	
2 pm	
3 pm	
4 pm	
5 pm	
6 pm	
7 pm	
8 pm	
9 pm	

Weekly Check-in

Review of the week

- [ ] Review How I'll know if I'm heading for a relapse
- [ ] Review My Character Defects
- [ ] Review People to stay in touch with
- [ ] Complete Spiritual Planner

What's gone well this week?

What are the biggest distractions in my life? How can I remove them?

Which part of the program do I need to prioritise next week?

How is my spiritual condition?

Spiritual Planner

My 2 main spiritual/recovery priorities for this week:

1.

2.

Spiritual and recovery-based activities for the week:

monday

tuesday

wednesday

thursday

friday

saturday

sunday

Date: _____   Sobriety Tracker: _____

journal

Do I need to forgive myself for anything?

_____
_____
_____
_____
_____
_____
_____
_____
_____
_____
_____
_____

personal inventory

'When we retire at night, we constructively review our day'

Was I resentful, selfish, dishonest or afraid?
_____

Do I owe an apology?
_____

Have I kept something to myself which should be discussed with another person at once?
_____

Was I kind and loving towards all?
_____

What could I have done better?
_____

Was I thinking about myself most of the time? Or was I thinking of what I could do for others, of what I could pack into the stream of life?
_____

I'm grateful for...

_____
_____
_____

today I accept...

_____
_____

☐ Prayer & meditation   ☐ Service/help someone

☐ Spiritual reading   ☐ Exercise

☐ Call someone   ☐ _____

'On awakening let us think about the twenty-four hours ahead...'

| 6 am |
| 7 am |
| 8 am |
| 9 am |
| 10 am |
| 11 am |
| 12 pm |
| 1 pm |
| 2 pm |
| 3 pm |
| 4 pm |
| 5 pm |
| 6 pm |
| 7 pm |
| 8 pm |
| 9 pm |

'A genuine gratitude for blessings received'

_____

_____

_____

_____

'God, grant me the serenity to accept the things I cannot change'

_____

_____

_____

- ☐ Prayer & meditation
- ☐ Service/help someone
- ☐ Spiritual reading
- ☐ Exercise
- ☐ Call someone
- ☐ ....

'...We consider our plans for the day'

	6 am
	7 am
	8 am
	9 am
	10 am
	11 am
	12 pm
	1 pm
	2 pm
	3 pm
	4 pm
	5 pm
	6 pm
	7 pm
	8 pm
	9 pm

Date: _____ Sobriety Tracker: _____

journal

Is there anything missing in my life?

_____

_____

_____

_____

_____

_____

_____

_____

_____

_____

_____

personal inventory

'When we retire at night, we constructively review our day'

Was I unkind (cruel, harsh, unfeeling)?

Who did I help today?

How did I show love to myself? Did I talk negatively to myself?

Am I obsessing about anything?

What am I proud of today?

Was I patient, kind and compassionate? What caused me to lose these attitudes? Do I owe anyone amends?

Date: _____   Sobriety Tracker: _____

journal

> What am I good at?
> What am I bad at?

_____
_____
_____
_____
_____
_____
_____
_____
_____
_____
_____
_____
_____
_____

personal inventory

'When we retire at night, we constructively review our day'

Was I resentful, selfish, dishonest or afraid?
_____
_____

Do I owe an apology?
_____
_____

Have I kept something to myself which should be discussed with another person at once?
_____
_____
_____

Was I kind and loving towards all?
_____
_____

What could I have done better?
_____
_____

Was I thinking about myself most of the time? Or was I thinking of what I could do for others, of what I could pack into the stream of life?
_____
_____
_____
_____

I'm grateful for...

_____
_____
_____
_____

today I accept...

_____
_____

☐ Prayer & meditation   ☐ Service/help someone

☐ Spiritual reading   ☐ Exercise

☐ Call someone   ☐ ....

'On awakening let us think about the twenty-four hours ahead...'

6 am
7 am
8 am
9 am
10 am
11 am
12 pm
1 pm
2 pm
3 pm
4 pm
5 pm
6 pm
7 pm
8 pm
9 pm

'A genuine gratitude for blessings received'

_____
_____
_____
_____

'God, grant me the serenity to accept the things I cannot change'

_____
_____
_____

☐ Prayer & meditation   ☐ Service/help someone

☐ Spiritual reading   ☐ Exercise

☐ Call someone   ☐ ....

'...We consider our plans for the day'

| 6 am |
| 7 am |
| 8 am |
| 9 am |
| 10 am |
| 11 am |
| 12 pm |
| 1 pm |
| 2 pm |
| 3 pm |
| 4 pm |
| 5 pm |
| 6 pm |
| 7 pm |
| 8 pm |
| 9 pm |

Date: _____   Sobriety Tracker: _____

journal

What's my happiest memory from my childhood?

_____
_____
_____
_____
_____
_____
_____
_____
_____
_____
_____
_____

personal inventory

'When we retire at night, we constructively review our day'

Did I do something for someone else today?

What did I accomplish today?

What have I done for my recovery today?

Am I taking care of my body?

What could I have done better?

Was I unloving today (cold, unresponsive, indifferent)?

Date: _____   Sobriety Tracker: _____

journal

How often do I ask other for help?

....
....
....
....
....
....
....
....
....
....
....
....
....
....
....
....

personal inventory

'When we retire at night, we constructively review our day'

Was I resentful, selfish, dishonest or afraid?
....
....

Do I owe an apology?
....
....

Have I kept something to myself which should be discussed with another person at once?
....
....
....
....

Was I kind and loving towards all?
....
....

What could I have done better?
....
....

Was I thinking about myself most of the time? Or was I thinking of what I could do for others, of what I could pack into the stream of life?
....
....
....
....
....
....

I'm grateful for...

....
....
....
....

today I accept...

....
....

☐ Prayer & meditation   ☐ Service/help someone

☐ Spiritual reading   ☐ Exercise

☐ Call someone   ☐ ....

'On awakening let us think about the twenty-four hours ahead...'

6 am
7 am
8 am
9 am
10 am
11 am
12 pm
1 pm
2 pm
3 pm
4 pm
5 pm
6 pm
7 pm
8 pm
9 pm

'A genuine gratitude for blessings received'

....
....
....
....

'God, grant me the serenity to accept the things I cannot change'

....
....
....
....

☐ Prayer & meditation   ☐ Service/help someone

☐ Spiritual reading   ☐ Exercise

☐ Call someone   ☐ ....

'...We consider our plans for the day'

	6 am
	7 am
	8 am
	9 am
	10 am
	11 am
	12 pm
	1 pm
	2 pm
	3 pm
	4 pm
	5 pm
	6 pm
	7 pm
	8 pm
	9 pm

journal

What does my ego get in the way of?

....
....
....
....
....
....
....
....
....
....
....
....
....
....
....

personal inventory

'When we retire at night, we constructively review our day'

Was I honest with others and myself today?
....
....

What can I celebrate? What could I have done differently?
....
....
....

How was my serenity? Did anything happen that caused me to lose it? What was my part in it?
....
....
....
....

Am I spending time on myself?
....
....

What did I do to connect with my higher power?
....
....

Did fear prevent me from doing anything today?
....
....

Date: _____   Sobriety Tracker: _____

journal

> Where can I give more of my time, money or support?

_____
_____
_____
_____
_____
_____
_____
_____
_____
_____
_____
_____
_____
_____
_____
_____

personal inventory

'When we retire at night, we constructively review our day'

Was I resentful, selfish, dishonest or afraid?	_____
Do I owe an apology?	_____
Have I kept something to myself which should be discussed with another person at once?	_____
Was I kind and loving towards all?	_____
What could I have done better?	_____
Was I thinking about myself most of the time? Or was I thinking of what I could do for others, of what I could pack into the stream of life?	_____

I'm grateful for...

_____
_____
_____
_____

today I accept...

_____
_____
_____

- ☐ Prayer & meditation
- ☐ Service/help someone
- ☐ Spiritual reading
- ☐ Exercise
- ☐ Call someone
- ☐ _____

'On awakening let us think about the twenty-four hours ahead...'

6 am	
7 am	
8 am	
9 am	
10 am	
11 am	
12 pm	
1 pm	
2 pm	
3 pm	
4 pm	
5 pm	
6 pm	
7 pm	
8 pm	
9 pm	

Weekly Check-in

Review of the week

- [ ] Review My Rock Bottom
- [ ] Review My Character Defects .
- [ ] Review People to stay in touch with
- [ ] Complete Spiritual Planner

What have I achieved this week?

What's not working? What am I willing to do about it?

What one thing can I do next week that will have the biggest positive impact on my life?

What do I need to make a decision about?

Spiritual Planner

My 2 main spiritual/recovery priorities for this week:

1.

2.

Spiritual and recovery-based activities for the week:

monday

tuesday

wednesday

thursday

friday

saturday

sunday

I know, dear God, that my part in this Program is going to be a thrilling and endless adventure. Despite all that has happened to me already, I know that I have just begun to grow. I have just begun to open to Your love. I have just begun to touch the varied lives You are using me to change. I have just begun to sense the possibilities ahead. And these possibilities, I am convinced, will continue to unfold into ever new and richer adventures, not only for the rest of my reborn days but also through eternity.

Possibilities Prayer

Bill P. and Lisa D. *The 12 Step Prayer Book. 2nd ed.* Center City, Minn.: Hazelden, 2004

journal

How can I be more authentic and true to myself?

personal inventory

'When we retire at night, we constructively review our day'

Was I resentful, selfish, dishonest or afraid?

Do I owe an apology?

Have I kept something to myself which should be discussed with another person at once?

Was I kind and loving towards all?

What could I have done better?

Was I thinking about myself most of the time? Or was I thinking of what I could do for others, of what I could pack into the stream of life?

I'm grateful for...

today I accept...

- ☐ Prayer & meditation
- ☐ Spiritual reading
- ☐ Call someone
- ☐ Service/help someone
- ☐ Exercise
- ☐ ....

'On awakening let us think about the twenty-four hours ahead...'

6 am
7 am
8 am
9 am
10 am
11 am
12 pm
1 pm
2 pm
3 pm
4 pm
5 pm
6 pm
7 pm
8 pm
9 pm

'A genuine gratitude for blessings received'

_____
_____
_____
_____
_____

'God, grant me the serenity to accept the things I cannot change'

_____
_____
_____
_____

- [ ] Prayer & meditation
- [ ] Service/help someone
- [ ] Spiritual reading
- [ ] Exercise
- [ ] Call someone
- [ ] ....

'...We consider our plans for the day'

	6 am
	7 am
	8 am
	9 am
	10 am
	11 am
	12 pm
	1 pm
	2 pm
	3 pm
	4 pm
	5 pm
	6 pm
	7 pm
	8 pm
	9 pm

Date: _____   Sobriety Tracker: _____

journal

> Do I enjoy talking about myself? How does it make me feel?

_____
_____
_____
_____
_____
_____
_____
_____
_____
_____
_____
_____
_____
_____
_____
_____

personal inventory

'When we retire at night, we constructively review our day'

Have I practiced any of my character defects?
_____

Am I keeping any secrets?
_____

Was I honest? Did I keep my word with everyone? Did I keep my word with myself?
_____

Am I trying to fill the void with external stimuli?
_____

Did I learn something useful today? Or was I a mental loafer?
_____

Was I concerned today with thoughts or behaviours linked to my addiction?
_____

journal

How can I be more creative?

I'm grateful for...

today I accept...

☐ Prayer & meditation   ☐ Service/help someone

☐ Spiritual reading   ☐ Exercise

☐ Call someone   ☐

'On awakening let us think about the twenty-four hours ahead...'

| 6 am |
| 7 am |
| 8 am |
| 9 am |
| 10 am |
| 11 am |
| 12 pm |
| 1 pm |
| 2 pm |
| 3 pm |
| 4 pm |
| 5 pm |
| 6 pm |
| 7 pm |
| 8 pm |
| 9 pm |

personal inventory

'When we retire at night, we constructively review our day'

Was I resentful, selfish, dishonest or afraid?

Do I owe an apology?

Have I kept something to myself which should be discussed with another person at once?

Was I kind and loving towards all?

What could I have done better?

Was I thinking about myself most of the time? Or was I thinking of what I could do for others, of what I could pack into the stream of life?

'A genuine gratitude for blessings received'

....
....
....

'God, grant me the serenity to accept the things I cannot change'

....
....
....

- ☐ Prayer & meditation
- ☐ Service/help someone
- ☐ Spiritual reading
- ☐ Exercise
- ☐ Call someone
- ☐ ....

'...We consider our plans for the day'

	6 am
	7 am
	8 am
	9 am
	10 am
	11 am
	12 pm
	1 pm
	2 pm
	3 pm
	4 pm
	5 pm
	6 pm
	7 pm
	8 pm
	9 pm

journal

What am I passionate about?

....
....
....
....
....
....
....
....
....
....
....
....
....

personal inventory

'When we retire at night, we constructively review our day'

How did I take care of my health (physical, emotional, spiritual) today?	
What have I enjoyed about today?	
How did I show love to others? Did I act unlovingly towards anyone?	
Who neds my prayers today?	
Am I holding any resentments?	
How is my spiritual condition?	

journal

What do I love to do?

I'm grateful for...

today I accept...

☐ Prayer & meditation   ☐ Service/help someone

☐ Spiritual reading   ☐ Exercise

☐ Call someone   ☐ ....

'On awakening let us think about the twenty-four hours ahead...'

6 am

7 am

8 am

9 am

10 am

11 am

12 pm

1 pm

2 pm

3 pm

4 pm

5 pm

6 pm

7 pm

8 pm

9 pm

personal inventory

'When we retire at night, we constructively review our day'

Was I resentful, selfish, dishonest or afraid?

Do I owe an apology?

Have I kept something to myself which should be discussed with another person at once?

Was I kind and loving towards all?

What could I have done better?

Was I thinking about myself most of the time? Or was I thinking of what I could do for others, of what I could pack into the stream of life?

genuine gratitude for blessings received'

....
....
....
....

'God, grant me the serenity to accept the things I cannot change'

....
....
....
....

☐ Prayer & meditation   ☐ Service/help someone

☐ Spiritual reading   ☐ Exercise

☐ Call someone   ☐ ....

..We consider our plans for the day'

	6 am
	7 am
	8 am
	9 am
	10 am
	11 am
	12 pm
	1 pm
	2 pm
	3 pm
	4 pm
	5 pm
	6 pm
	7 pm
	8 pm
	9 pm

Date: _____   Sobriety Tracker: _____

journal

How much sleep do I need?
How much am I getting?

....
....
....
....
....
....
....
....
....
....
....
....
....

personal inventory

'When we retire at night, we constructively review our day'

Was I unkind (cruel, harsh, unfeeling)?

Who did I help today?

How did I show love to myself? Did I talk negatively to myself?

Am I obsessing about anything?

What am I proud of today?

Was I patient, kind and compassionate? What caused me to lose these attitudes? Do I owe anyone amends?

Date: _____   Sobriety Tracker: _____

journal

Do I have any recurring dreams?

_____
_____
_____
_____
_____
_____
_____
_____
_____
_____
_____

personal inventory

'When we retire at night, we constructively review our day'

Was I resentful, selfish, dishonest or afraid?
_____
_____

Do I owe an apology?
_____
_____

Have I kept something to myself which should be discussed with another person at once?
_____
_____
_____

Was I kind and loving towards all?
_____
_____

What could I have done better?
_____
_____

Was I thinking about myself most of the time? Or was I thinking of what I could do for others, of what I could pack into the stream of life?
_____
_____
_____
_____
_____

I'm grateful for...

_____
_____
_____
_____

today I accept...

_____
_____
_____

☐ Prayer & meditation ☐ Service/help someone

☐ Spiritual reading ☐ Exercise

☐ Call someone ☐ ....

'On awakening let us think about the twenty-four hours ahead...'

6 am
7 am
8 am
9 am
10 am
11 am
12 pm
1 pm
2 pm
3 pm
4 pm
5 pm
6 pm
7 pm
8 pm
9 pm

Weekly Check-in

Review of the week

- ☑ Review My Triggers
- ☑ Review My Rescue Plan
- ☑ Review People to stay in touch with
- ☑ Complete Spiritual Planner

What's working and why is it working?

What part of my recovery have I been neglecting?

What do I need to pay more attention to?

Have I had fun this week? How can I have more fun?

Spiritual Planner

My 2 main spiritual/recovery priorities for this week:

1.

2.

Spiritual and recovery-based activities for the week:

monday

tuesday

wednesday

thursday

friday

saturday

sunday

Date: _____   Sobriety Tracker: _____

journal

Who inspires me? Why?

_____
_____
_____
_____
_____
_____
_____
_____
_____
_____
_____
_____
_____
_____

personal inventory

'When we retire at night, we constructively review our day'

Was I resentful, selfish, dishonest or afraid?

Do I owe an apology?

Have I kept something to myself which should be discussed with another person at once?

Was I kind and loving towards all?

What could I have done better?

Was I thinking about myself most of the time? Or was I thinking of what I could do for others, of what I could pack into the stream of life?

I'm grateful for...

_____
_____
_____

today I accept...

_____
_____
_____

☐ Prayer & meditation   ☐ Service/help someone

☐ Spiritual reading   ☐ Exercise

☐ Call someone   ☐ ....

'On awakening let us think about the twenty-four hours ahead...'

6 am
7 am
8 am
9 am
10 am
11 am
12 pm
1 pm
2 pm
3 pm
4 pm
5 pm
6 pm
7 pm
8 pm
9 pm

'A genuine gratitude for blessings received'

....
....
....
....

'God, grant me the serenity to accept the things I cannot change'

....
....
....
....

☐ Prayer & meditation ☐ Service/help someone

☐ Spiritual reading ☐ Exercise

☐ Call someone ☐ ....

'...We consider our plans for the day'

6 am

7 am

8 am

9 am

10 am

11 am

12 pm

1 pm

2 pm

3 pm

4 pm

5 pm

6 pm

7 pm

8 pm

9 pm

Date: _____ Sobriety Tracker: _____

journal

How do I want others to see me?

....
....
....
....
....
....
....
....
....
....
....
....
....
....

personal inventory

'When we retire at night, we constructively review our day'

Did I do something for someone else today?

What did I accomplish today?

What have I done for my recovery today?

Am I taking care of my body?

What could I have done better?

Was I unloving today (cold, unresponsive, indifferent)?

Date: _____ Sobriety Tracker: _____

journal

What's my greatest strength?

_____
_____
_____
_____
_____
_____
_____
_____
_____
_____
_____
_____
_____

personal inventory

'When we retire at night, we constructively review our day'

Was I resentful, selfish, dishonest or afraid?

Do I owe an apology?

Have I kept something to myself which should be discussed with another person at once?

Was I kind and loving towards all?

What could I have done better?

Was I thinking about myself most of the time? Or was I thinking of what I could do for others, of what I could pack into the stream of life?

I'm grateful for...

_____
_____
_____
_____

today I accept...

_____
_____
_____

☐ Prayer & meditation   ☐ Service/help someone

☐ Spiritual reading   ☐ Exercise

☐ Call someone   ☐ ....

'On awakening let us think about the twenty-four hours ahead...'

6 am
7 am
8 am
9 am
10 am
11 am
12 pm
1 pm
2 pm
3 pm
4 pm
5 pm
6 pm
7 pm
8 pm
9 pm

'A genuine gratitude for blessings received'

....
....
....
....

'God, grant me the serenity to accept the things I cannot change'

....
....
....
....

☐ Prayer & meditation   ☐ Service/help someone

☐ Spiritual reading   ☐ Exercise

☐ Call someone   ☐ ....

'...We consider our plans for the day'

	6 am
	7 am
	8 am
	9 am
	10 am
	11 am
	12 pm
	1 pm
	2 pm
	3 pm
	4 pm
	5 pm
	6 pm
	7 pm
	8 pm
	9 pm

Date: _____ Sobriety Tracker: _____

journal

How would my higher power have me be today?

....
....
....
....
....
....
....
....
....
....
....
....
....

personal inventory

'When we retire at night, we constructively review our day'

Was I honest with others and myself today?

What can I celebrate? What could I have done differently?

How was my serenity? Did anything happen that caused me to lose it? What was my part in it?

Am I spending time on myself?

What did I do to connect with my higher power?

Did fear prevent me from doing anything today?

Date: _____ Sobriety Tracker: _____

journal

What do I want to achieve today?

_____
_____
_____
_____
_____
_____
_____
_____
_____
_____
_____
_____

personal inventory

'When we retire at night, we constructively review our day'

Was I resentful, selfish, dishonest or afraid?
_____

Do I owe an apology?
_____

Have I kept something to myself which should be discussed with another person at once?
_____

Was I kind and loving towards all?
_____

What could I have done better?
_____

Was I thinking about myself most of the time? Or was I thinking of what I could do for others, of what I could pack into the stream of life?
_____

I'm grateful for...

_____
_____
_____

today I accept...

_____
_____

- [ ] Prayer & meditation
- [ ] Service/help someone
- [ ] Spiritual reading
- [ ] Exercise
- [ ] Call someone
- [ ] ....

'On awakening let us think about the twenty-four hours ahead...'

6 am
7 am
8 am
9 am
10 am
11 am
12 pm
1 pm
2 pm
3 pm
4 pm
5 pm
6 pm
7 pm
8 pm
9 pm

'A genuine gratitude for blessings received'

_____

_____

_____

_____

'God, grant me the serenity to accept the things I cannot change'

_____

_____

_____

_____

☐ Prayer & meditation   ☐ Service/help someone

☐ Spiritual reading   ☐ Exercise

☐ Call someone   ☐ ....

'...We consider our plans for the day'

	6 am
	7 am
	8 am
	9 am
	10 am
	11 am
	12 pm
	1 pm
	2 pm
	3 pm
	4 pm
	5 pm
	6 pm
	7 pm
	8 pm
	9 pm

journal

What character defect do I particularly want to avoid today?

_____

_____

_____

_____

_____

_____

_____

_____

_____

_____

_____

_____

_____

_____

_____

personal inventory

'When we retire at night, we constructively review our day'

Have I practiced any of my character defects?

_____

Am I keeping any secrets?

_____

Was I honest? Did I keep my word with everyone? Did I keep my word with myself?

_____

Am I trying to fill the void with external stimuli?

_____

Did I learn something useful today? Or was I a mental loafer?

_____

Was I concerned today with thoughts or behaviours linked to my addiction?

_____

Date: _____ Sobriety Tracker: _____

journal

What do I think about myself?

_____
_____
_____
_____
_____
_____
_____
_____
_____
_____
_____
_____
_____
_____

personal inventory

'When we retire at night, we constructively review our day'

Was I resentful, selfish, dishonest or afraid?	
Do I owe an apology?	
Have I kept something to myself which should be discussed with another person at once?	
Was I kind and loving towards all?	
What could I have done better?	
Was I thinking about myself most of the time? Or was I thinking of what I could do for others, of what I could pack into the stream of life?	

I'm grateful for...

_____
_____
_____

today I accept...

_____
_____

☐ Prayer & meditation   ☐ Service/help someone

☐ Spiritual reading   ☐ Exercise

☐ Call someone   ☐ ....

'On awakening let us think about the twenty-four hours ahead...'

6 am
7 am
8 am
9 am
10 am
11 am
12 pm
1 pm
2 pm
3 pm
4 pm
5 pm
6 pm
7 pm
8 pm
9 pm

Weekly Check-in

Review of the week

- [ ] Review What would happen if I relapse
- [ ] Review My Character Defects
- [ ] Review People to stay in touch with
- [ ] Complete Spiritual Planner

What's made me happy this week?

What's been most difficult this week? Do I need to change something?

What do I need to start doing? What do I need to stop doing?

How can I prioritise my time better?

Spiritual Planner

My 2 main spiritual/recovery priorities for this week:

1.

2.

Spiritual and recovery-based activities for the week:

monday

tuesday

wednesday

thursday

friday

saturday

sunday

journal

What's currently worrying me?

personal inventory

'When we retire at night, we constructively review our day'

Was I resentful, selfish, dishonest or afraid?

Do I owe an apology?

Have I kept something to myself which should be discussed with another person at once?

Was I kind and loving towards all?

What could I have done better?

Was I thinking about myself most of the time? Or was I thinking of what I could do for others, of what I could pack into the stream of life?

I'm grateful for...

today I accept...

☐ Prayer & meditation   ☐ Service/help someone

☐ Spiritual reading   ☐ Exercise

☐ Call someone   ☐ ....

'On awakening let us think about the twenty-four hours ahead...'

6 am

7 am

8 am

9 am

10 am

11 am

12 pm

1 pm

2 pm

3 pm

4 pm

5 pm

6 pm

7 pm

8 pm

9 pm

'A genuine gratitude for blessings received'

....
....
....

*'God, grant me the serenity to accept the
things I cannot change'*

....
....

- ☐ Prayer & meditation
- ☐ Service/help someone
- ☐ Spiritual reading
- ☐ Exercise
- ☐ Call someone
- ☐ ....

'...We consider our plans for the day'

	6 am
	7 am
	8 am
	9 am
	10 am
	11 am
	12 pm
	1 pm
	2 pm
	3 pm
	4 pm
	5 pm
	6 pm
	7 pm
	8 pm
	9 pm

journal

> How can I create more energy?

....
....
....
....
....
....
....
....
....
....
....
....
....

personal inventory

'When we retire at night, we constructively review our day'

How did I take care of my health (physical, emotional, spiritual) today?

What have I enjoyed about today?

How did I show love to others? Did I act unlovingly towards anyone?

Who neds my prayers today?

Am I holding any resentments?

How is my spiritual condition?

Date: _____ Sobriety Tracker: _____

journal

Do I need to expand my friendship group? If so, how?

_____
_____
_____
_____
_____
_____
_____
_____
_____
_____
_____
_____
_____
_____
_____
_____

personal inventory

'When we retire at night, we constructively review our day'

Was I resentful, selfish, dishonest or afraid?
_____

Do I owe an apology?
_____

Have I kept something to myself which should be discussed with another person at once?
_____

Was I kind and loving towards all?
_____

What could I have done better?
_____

Was I thinking about myself most of the time? Or was I thinking of what I could do for others, of what I could pack into the stream of life?
_____

I'm grateful for...
_____
_____
_____

today I accept...
_____
_____
_____

☐ Prayer & meditation   ☐ Service/help someone

☐ Spiritual reading   ☐ Exercise

☐ Call someone   ☐ _____

'On awakening let us think about the twenty-four hours ahead...'

6 am	
7 am	
8 am	
9 am	
10 am	
11 am	
12 pm	
1 pm	
2 pm	
3 pm	
4 pm	
5 pm	
6 pm	
7 pm	
8 pm	
9 pm	

'A genuine gratitude for blessings received'

....

....

....

'God, grant me the serenity to accept the things I cannot change'

....

....

....

....

☐ Prayer & meditation ☐ Service/help someone

☐ Spiritual reading ☐ Exercise

☐ Call someone ☐ ....

'...We consider our plans for the day'

6 am

7 am

8 am

9 am

10 am

11 am

12 pm

1 pm

2 pm

3 pm

4 pm

5 pm

6 pm

7 pm

8 pm

9 pm

Date: _____   Sobriety Tracker: _____

journal

What kind of person would my higher power have me be?

....

....

....

....

....

....

....

....

....

....

....

....

personal inventory

'When we retire at night, we constructively review our day'

Was I unkind (cruel, harsh, unfeeling)?

Who did I help today?

How did I show love to myself? Did I talk negatively to myself?

Am I obsessing about anything?

What am I proud of today?

Was I patient, kind and compassionate? What caused me to lose these attitudes? Do I owe anyone amends?

Date: _____ Sobriety Tracker: _____

journal

What do I want to do with the rest of my life?

personal inventory

'When we retire at night, we constructively review our day'

Was I resentful, selfish, dishonest or afraid?	
Do I owe an apology?	
Have I kept something to myself which should be discussed with another person at once?	
Was I kind and loving towards all?	
What could I have done better?	
Was I thinking about myself most of the time? Or was I thinking of what I could do for others, of what I could pack into the stream of life?	

I'm grateful for...

_____

_____

_____

today I accept...

_____

_____

_____

☐ Prayer & meditation   ☐ Service/help someone

☐ Spiritual reading   ☐ Exercise

☐ Call someone   ☐ ....

'On awakening let us think about the twenty-four hours ahead...'

6 am	
7 am	
8 am	
9 am	
10 am	
11 am	
12 pm	
1 pm	
2 pm	
3 pm	
4 pm	
5 pm	
6 pm	
7 pm	
8 pm	
9 pm	

'A genuine gratitude for blessings received'

....
....
....
....
....

'God, grant me the serenity to accept the things I cannot change'

....
....
....

☐ Prayer & meditation   ☐ Service/help someone

☐ Spiritual reading   ☐ Exercise

☐ Call someone   ☐ ....

'...We consider our plans for the day'

6 am
7 am
8 am
9 am
10 am
11 am
12 pm
1 pm
2 pm
3 pm
4 pm
5 pm
6 pm
7 pm
8 pm
9 pm

journal

> Do I care about others? Who? Why?

....
....
....
....
....
....
....
....
....
....
....
....
....
....

personal inventory

'When we retire at night, we constructively review our day'

Did I do something for someone else today?

What did I accomplish today?

What have I done for my recovery today?

Am I taking care of my body?

What could I have done better?

Was I unloving today (cold, unresponsive, indifferent)?

journal

How do I want to be remembered?

_____
_____
_____
_____
_____
_____
_____
_____
_____
_____
_____
_____
_____
_____
_____
_____

personal inventory

'When we retire at night, we constructively review our day'

Was I resentful, selfish, dishonest or afraid?	....
Do I owe an apology?	....
Have I kept something to myself which should be discussed with another person at once?	....
Was I kind and loving towards all?	....
What could I have done better?	....
Was I thinking about myself most of the time? Or was I thinking of what I could do for others, of what I could pack into the stream of life?	....

I'm grateful for...

_____
_____
_____

today I accept...

_____
_____
_____

☐ Prayer & meditation   ☐ Service/help someone

☐ Spiritual reading   ☐ Exercise

☐ Call someone   ☐ ....

'On awakening let us think about the twenty-four hours ahead...'

6 am	
7 am	
8 am	
9 am	
10 am	
11 am	
12 pm	
1 pm	
2 pm	
3 pm	
4 pm	
5 pm	
6 pm	
7 pm	
8 pm	
9 pm	

Weekly Check-in

Review of the week

- [ ] Review My vision for the future
- [ ] Review My Rescue Plan
- [ ] Review People to stay in touch with
- [ ] Complete Spiritual Planner

What's been the biggest positive this week?

What fears have been holding me back?

Do I need to ask for some help next week? Is there anyone who needs my help?

Have I been looking after myself this week?

Spiritual Planner

My 2 main spiritual/recovery priorities for this week:

1.

2.

Spiritual and recovery-based activities for the week:

monday

tuesday

wednesday

thursday

friday

saturday

sunday

Date: _____ Sobriety Tracker: _____

journal

> Who or what always makes me laugh? Why?

_____
_____
_____
_____
_____
_____
_____
_____
_____
_____
_____
_____
_____
_____

personal inventory

'When we retire at night, we constructively review our day'

Was I resentful, selfish, dishonest or afraid?
_____

Do I owe an apology?
_____

Have I kept something to myself which should be discussed with another person at once?
_____
_____
_____

Was I kind and loving towards all?
_____

What could I have done better?
_____

Was I thinking about myself most of the time? Or was I thinking of what I could do for others, of what I could pack into the stream of life?
_____
_____
_____

I'm grateful for...

_____
_____
_____

today I accept...

_____
_____

☐ Prayer & meditation   ☐ Service/help someone

☐ Spiritual reading   ☐ Exercise

☐ Call someone   ☐ ....

'On awakening let us think about the twenty-four hours ahead...'

6 am
7 am
8 am
9 am
10 am
11 am
12 pm
1 pm
2 pm
3 pm
4 pm
5 pm
6 pm
7 pm
8 pm
9 pm

'A genuine gratitude for blessings received'

....
....
....
....
....

*'God, grant me the serenity to accept the
things I cannot change'*

....
....
....
....

☐ Prayer &
  meditation

☐ Service/help
  someone

☐ Spiritual
  reading

☐ Exercise

☐ Call someone

☐ ....

'...We consider our plans for the day'

	6 am
	7 am
	8 am
	9 am
	10 am
	11 am
	12 pm
	1 pm
	2 pm
	3 pm
	4 pm
	5 pm
	6 pm
	7 pm
	8 pm
	9 pm

Date: _____   Sobriety Tracker: _____

journal

How can I be more flexible?

....
....
....
....
....
....
....
....
....
....
....
....
....
....

personal inventory

*'When we retire at night, we
constructively review our day'*

Was I honest with others and myself today?

....
....

What can I celebrate? What could I have done differently?

....
....
....

How was my serenity? Did anything happen that caused me to lose it? What was my part in it?

....
....
....
....
....

Am I spending time on myself?

....
....

What did I do to connect with my higher power?

....
....

Did fear prevent me from doing anything today?

....
....

Date: _____   Sobriety Tracker: _____

journal

> Can I accept compliments easily?
> How do they make me feel?

_____
_____
_____
_____
_____
_____
_____
_____
_____
_____
_____
_____
_____
_____
_____
_____

personal inventory

'When we retire at night, we constructively review our day'

Was I resentful, selfish, dishonest or afraid?
_____
_____

Do I owe an apology?
_____
_____

Have I kept something to myself which should be discussed with another person at once?
_____
_____
_____
_____

Was I kind and loving towards all?
_____
_____

What could I have done better?
_____
_____

Was I thinking about myself most of the time? Or was I thinking of what I could do for others, of what I could pack into the stream of life?
_____
_____
_____
_____
_____

I'm grateful for...

_____
_____
_____

today I accept...

_____
_____
_____

☐ Prayer & meditation   ☐ Service/help someone

☐ Spiritual reading   ☐ Exercise

☐ Call someone   ☐ ....

'On awakening let us think about the twenty-four hours ahead...'

6 am	
7 am	
8 am	
9 am	
10 am	
11 am	
12 pm	
1 pm	
2 pm	
3 pm	
4 pm	
5 pm	
6 pm	
7 pm	
8 pm	
9 pm	

'A genuine gratitude for blessings received'

....
....
....
....
....

'God, grant me the serenity to accept the things I cannot change'

....
....
....
....

☐ Prayer & meditation   ☐ Service/help someone

☐ Spiritual reading   ☐ Exercise

☐ Call someone   ☐ ....

'...We consider our plans for the day'

6 am
7 am
8 am
9 am
10 am
11 am
12 pm
1 pm
2 pm
3 pm
4 pm
5 pm
6 pm
7 pm
8 pm
9 pm

journal

How can I 'keep it in the day' more?

....
....
....
....
....
....
....
....
....
....
....
....
....
....
....

personal inventory

'When we retire at night, we constructively review our day'

Have I practiced any of my character defects?

Am I keeping any secrets?

Was I honest? Did I keep my word with everyone? Did I keep my word with myself?

Am I trying to fill the void with external stimuli?

Did I learn something useful today? Or was I a mental loafer?

Was I concerned today with thoughts or behaviours linked to my addiction?

journal

How could I be of service today?

I'm grateful for...

today I accept...

☐ Prayer & meditation   ☐ Service/help someone

☐ Spiritual reading   ☐ Exercise

☐ Call someone   ☐ ....

'On awakening let us think about the twenty-four hours ahead...'

6 am

7 am

8 am

9 am

10 am

11 am

12 pm

1 pm

2 pm

3 pm

4 pm

5 pm

6 pm

7 pm

8 pm

9 pm

personal inventory

'When we retire at night, we constructively review our day'

Was I resentful, selfish, dishonest or afraid?

Do I owe an apology?

Have I kept something to myself which should be discussed with another person at once?

Was I kind and loving towards all?

What could I have done better?

Was I thinking about myself most of the time? Or was I thinking of what I could do for others, of what I could pack into the stream of life?

'A genuine gratitude for blessings received'

....
....
....

'God, grant me the serenity to accept the things I cannot change'

....
....

journal

> How would my best friend describe me?

- ☐ Prayer & meditation
- ☐ Service/help someone
- ☐ Spiritual reading
- ☐ Exercise
- ☐ Call someone
- ☐ ....

....
....
....
....
....
....
....
....
....
....
....
....

'...We consider our plans for the day'

6 am	
7 am	
8 am	
9 am	
10 am	
11 am	
12 pm	
1 pm	
2 pm	
3 pm	
4 pm	
5 pm	
6 pm	
7 pm	
8 pm	
9 pm	

personal inventory

'When we retire at night, we constructively review our day'

How did I take care of my health (physical, emotional, spiritual) today?

What have I enjoyed about today?

How did I show love to others? Did I act unlovingly towards anyone?

Who neds my prayers today?

Am I holding any resentments?

How is my spiritual condition?

Date: _____ Sobriety Tracker: _____

journal

> What period of my life did I dislike the most? Why?

_____
_____
_____
_____
_____
_____
_____
_____
_____
_____
_____
_____
_____

personal inventory

'When we retire at night, we constructively review our day'

Was I resentful, selfish, dishonest or afraid?
_____

Do I owe an apology?
_____

Have I kept something to myself which should be discussed with another person at once?
_____

Was I kind and loving towards all?
_____

What could I have done better?
_____

Was I thinking about myself most of the time? Or was I thinking of what I could do for others, of what I could pack into the stream of life?
_____

I'm grateful for...

_____
_____
_____

today I accept...

_____
_____

☐ Prayer & meditation   ☐ Service/help someone

☐ Spiritual reading   ☐ Exercise

☐ Call someone   ☐ ....

'On awakening let us think about the twenty-four hours ahead...'

6 am
7 am
8 am
9 am
10 am
11 am
12 pm
1 pm
2 pm
3 pm
4 pm
5 pm
6 pm
7 pm
8 pm
9 pm

Weekly Check-in

Review of the week

- ☐ Review How I'll know if I'm heading for a relapse
- ☐ Review My Character Defects
- ☐ Review People to stay in touch with
- ☐ Complete Spiritual Planner

What's gone well this week?

What are the biggest distractions in my life? How can I remove them?

Which part of the program do I need to prioritise next week?

How is my spiritual condition?

Spiritual Planner

My 2 main spiritual/recovery priorities for this week:

1.

2.

Spiritual and recovery-based activities for the week:

monday

tuesday

wednesday

thursday

friday

saturday

sunday

journal

How can I be a better friend?

personal inventory

'When we retire at night, we constructively review our day'

Was I resentful, selfish, dishonest or afraid?

Do I owe an apology?

Have I kept something to myself which should be discussed with another person at once?

Was I kind and loving towards all?

What could I have done better?

Was I thinking about myself most of the time? Or was I thinking of what I could do for others, of what I could pack into the stream of life?

I'm grateful for...

today I accept...

- [ ] Prayer & meditation
- [ ] Spiritual reading
- [ ] Call someone
- [ ] Service/help someone
- [ ] Exercise
- [ ] ....

'On awakening let us think about the twenty-four hours ahead...'

6 am

7 am

8 am

9 am

10 am

11 am

12 pm

1 pm

2 pm

3 pm

4 pm

5 pm

6 pm

7 pm

8 pm

9 pm

genuine gratitude for blessings received'

....
....
....
....
....
....

'God, grant me the serenity to accept the
things I cannot change'

....
....
....
....

☐ Prayer &
   meditation

☐ Service/help
   someone

☐ Spiritual
   reading

☐ Exercise

☐ Call someone

☐ ....

...We consider our plans for the day'

	6 am
	7 am
	8 am
	9 am
	10 am
	11 am
	12 pm
	1 pm
	2 pm
	3 pm
	4 pm
	5 pm
	6 pm
	7 pm
	8 pm
	9 pm

journal

Which of the tools in the
checklist will best serve me
today?

....
....
....
....
....
....
....
....
....
....
....
....
....

personal inventory

'When we retire at night, we
constructively review our day'

Was I unkind
(cruel, harsh,
unfeeling)?

....
....

Who did I help
today?

....
....

How did I show
love to myself?
Did I talk
negatively to
myself?

....
....
....

Am I obsessing
about anything?

....
....

What am I
proud of today?

....
....

Was I patient,
kind and
compassionate?
What caused me
to lose these
attitudes? Do I
owe anyone
amends?

....
....
....
....
....

Date: _____   Sobriety Tracker: _____

journal

What's the best advice I've ever received?

_____
_____
_____
_____
_____
_____
_____
_____
_____
_____
_____
_____
_____

personal inventory

'When we retire at night, we constructively review our day'

Was I resentful, selfish, dishonest or afraid?
_____

Do I owe an apology?
_____

Have I kept something to myself which should be discussed with another person at once?
_____

Was I kind and loving towards all?
_____

What could I have done better?
_____

Was I thinking about myself most of the time? Or was I thinking of what I could do for others, of what I could pack into the stream of life?
_____

I'm grateful for...

....
....
....
....

today I accept...

....
....
....

☐ Prayer & meditation   ☐ Service/help someone

☐ Spiritual reading   ☐ Exercise

☐ Call someone   ☐ ....

'On awakening let us think about the twenty-four hours ahead...'

6 am	
7 am	
8 am	
9 am	
10 am	
11 am	
12 pm	
1 pm	
2 pm	
3 pm	
4 pm	
5 pm	
6 pm	
7 pm	
8 pm	
9 pm	

'A genuine gratitude for blessings received'

....
....
....
....

*'God, grant me the serenity to accept the
things I cannot change'*

....
....
....
....

☐ Prayer &
  meditation

☐ Service/help
  someone

☐ Spiritual
  reading

☐ Exercise

☐ Call someone

☐
  ....

'...We consider our plans for the day'

	6 am
	7 am
	8 am
	9 am
	10 am
	11 am
	12 pm
	1 pm
	2 pm
	3 pm
	4 pm
	5 pm
	6 pm
	7 pm
	8 pm
	9 pm

Date: _____   Sobriety Tracker: _____

journal

What would I love to
experience just for fun?

....
....
....
....
....
....
....
....
....
....
....
....
....
....
....

personal inventory

*'When we retire at night, we
constructively review our day'*

Did I do
something for
someone else
today?

What did I
accomplish
today?

What have I
done for my
recovery today?

Am I taking care
of my body?

What could I
have done
better?

Was I unloving
today (cold,
unresponsive,
indifferent)?

Date: _____   Sobriety Tracker: _____

journal

> What's the biggest risk I've taken?

_____
_____
_____
_____
_____
_____
_____
_____
_____
_____
_____
_____
_____

personal inventory

'When we retire at night, we constructively review our day'

Was I resentful, selfish, dishonest or afraid?	_____
Do I owe an apology?	_____
Have I kept something to myself which should be discussed with another person at once?	_____
Was I kind and loving towards all?	_____
What could I have done better?	_____
Was I thinking about myself most of the time? Or was I thinking of what I could do for others, of what I could pack into the stream of life?	_____

I'm grateful for...

_____
_____
_____
_____

today I accept...

_____
_____
_____

☐ Prayer & meditation ☐ Service/help someone

☐ Spiritual reading ☐ Exercise

☐ Call someone ☐ ....

'On awakening let us think about the twenty-four hours ahead...'

6 am	
7 am	
8 am	
9 am	
10 am	
11 am	
12 pm	
1 pm	
2 pm	
3 pm	
4 pm	
5 pm	
6 pm	
7 pm	
8 pm	
9 pm	

'A genuine gratitude for blessings received'

....
....
....
....

'God, grant me the serenity to accept the things I cannot change'

....
....
....
....

☐ Prayer & meditation   ☐ Service/help someone

☐ Spiritual reading   ☐ Exercise

☐ Call someone   ☐ ....

'...We consider our plans for the day'

6 am
7 am
8 am
9 am
10 am
11 am
12 pm
1 pm
2 pm
3 pm
4 pm
5 pm
6 pm
7 pm
8 pm
9 pm

journal

What new skills would I like to develop?

....
....
....
....
....
....
....
....
....
....
....
....
....
....

personal inventory

'When we retire at night, we constructively review our day'

Was I honest with others and myself today?

What can I celebrate? What could I have done differently?

How was my serenity? Did anything happen that caused me to lose it? What was my part in it?

Am I spending time on myself?

What did I do to connect with my higher power?

Did fear prevent me from doing anything today?

Date: _____   Sobriety Tracker: _____

journal

> What's on my mind?
> What's in my heart?

_____
_____
_____
_____
_____
_____
_____
_____
_____
_____
_____
_____

personal inventory

'When we retire at night, we constructively review our day'

Was I resentful, selfish, dishonest or afraid?
_____

Do I owe an apology?
_____

Have I kept something to myself which should be discussed with another person at once?
_____

Was I kind and loving towards all?
_____

What could I have done better?
_____

Was I thinking about myself most of the time? Or was I thinking of what I could do for others, of what I could pack into the stream of life?
_____

I'm grateful for...

_____
_____
_____
_____

today I accept...

_____
_____
_____

☐ Prayer & meditation   ☐ Service/help someone

☐ Spiritual reading   ☐ Exercise

☐ Call someone   ☐ _____

'On awakening let us think about the twenty-four hours ahead...'

6 am
7 am
8 am
9 am
10 am
11 am
12 pm
1 pm
2 pm
3 pm
4 pm
5 pm
6 pm
7 pm
8 pm
9 pm

Weekly Check-in

Review of the week

- [ ] Review My Rock Bottom
- [ ] Review My Character Defects
- [ ] Review People to stay in touch with
- [ ] Complete Spiritual Planner

What have I achieved this week?

What's not working? What am I willing to do about it?

What one thing can I do next week that will have the biggest positive impact on my life?

What do I need to make a decision about?

Spiritual Planner

My 2 main spiritual/recovery priorities for this week:

1.

2.

Spiritual and recovery-based activities for the week:

monday

tuesday

wednesday

thursday

friday

saturday

sunday

journal

Is there anyone who I need to give a second chance to?

personal inventory

'When we retire at night, we constructively review our day'

Was I resentful, selfish, dishonest or afraid?

Do I owe an apology?

Have I kept something to myself which should be discussed with another person at once?

Was I kind and loving towards all?

What could I have done better?

Was I thinking about myself most of the time? Or was I thinking of what I could do for others, of what I could pack into the stream of life?

I'm grateful for...

today I accept...

- ☐ Prayer & meditation
- ☐ Service/help someone
- ☐ Spiritual reading
- ☐ Exercise
- ☐ Call someone
- ☐ ....

'On awakening let us think about the twenty-four hours ahead...'

6 am
7 am
8 am
9 am
10 am
11 am
12 pm
1 pm
2 pm
3 pm
4 pm
5 pm
6 pm
7 pm
8 pm
9 pm

'A genuine gratitude for blessings received'

....
....
....
....

'God, grant me the serenity to accept the things I cannot change'

....
....
....
....

journal

> Who do I need to set healthy boundaries with?

....
....
....
....
....
....
....
....
....
....
....
....
....
....
....

- [ ] Prayer & meditation
- [ ] Service/help someone
- [ ] Spiritual reading
- [ ] Exercise
- [ ] Call someone
- [ ] ....

'...We consider our plans for the day'

6 am	
7 am	
8 am	
9 am	
10 am	
11 am	
12 pm	
1 pm	
2 pm	
3 pm	
4 pm	
5 pm	
6 pm	
7 pm	
8 pm	
9 pm	

personal inventory

'When we retire at night, we constructively review our day'

Have I practiced any of my character defects?
....

Am I keeping any secrets?
....

Was I honest? Did I keep my word with everyone? Did I keep my word with myself?
....

Am I trying to fill the void with external stimuli?
....

Did I learn something useful today? Or was I a mental loafer?
....

Was I concerned today with thoughts or behaviours linked to my addiction?
....

Date: _____ Sobriety Tracker: _____

journal

Who have I been avoiding? Why?

_____
_____
_____
_____
_____
_____
_____
_____
_____
_____
_____
_____
_____
_____

personal inventory

'When we retire at night, we constructively review our day'

Was I resentful, selfish, dishonest or afraid?	_____
Do I owe an apology?	_____
Have I kept something to myself which should be discussed with another person at once?	_____
Was I kind and loving towards all?	_____
What could I have done better?	_____
Was I thinking about myself most of the time? Or was I thinking of what I could do for others, of what I could pack into the stream of life?	_____

I'm grateful for...

....
....
....
....

today I accept...

....
....
....

☐ Prayer & meditation   ☐ Service/help someone

☐ Spiritual reading   ☐ Exercise

☐ Call someone   ☐ ....

'On awakening let us think about the twenty-four hours ahead...'

6 am	
7 am	
8 am	
9 am	
10 am	
11 am	
12 pm	
1 pm	
2 pm	
3 pm	
4 pm	
5 pm	
6 pm	
7 pm	
8 pm	
9 pm	

'A genuine gratitude for blessings received'

....
....
....
....

'God, grant me the serenity to accept the things I cannot change'

....
....
....
....

☐ Prayer & meditation   ☐ Service/help someone

☐ Spiritual reading   ☐ Exercise

☐ Call someone   ☐ ....

'…We consider our plans for the day'

6 am	
7 am	
8 am	
9 am	
10 am	
11 am	
12 pm	
1 pm	
2 pm	
3 pm	
4 pm	
5 pm	
6 pm	
7 pm	
8 pm	
9 pm	

journal

What baggage do I have that holds me back?

....
....
....
....
....
....
....
....
....
....
....
....
....

personal inventory

'When we retire at night, we constructively review our day'

How did I take care of my health (physical, emotional, spiritual) today?

What have I enjoyed about today?

How did I show love to others? Did I act unlovingly towards anyone?

Who neds my prayers today?

Am I holding any resentments?

How is my spiritual condition?

Date: _____   Sobriety Tracker: _____

journal

> What nourishes my soul?

_____
_____
_____
_____
_____
_____
_____
_____
_____
_____
_____
_____
_____
_____

personal inventory

'When we retire at night, we constructively review our day'

Was I resentful, selfish, dishonest or afraid?
_____

Do I owe an apology?
_____

Have I kept something to myself which should be discussed with another person at once?
_____

Was I kind and loving towards all?
_____

What could I have done better?
_____

Was I thinking about myself most of the time? Or was I thinking of what I could do for others, of what I could pack into the stream of life?
_____

I'm grateful for...

_____
_____
_____

today I accept...

_____
_____

☐ Prayer & meditation   ☐ Service/help someone

☐ Spiritual reading   ☐ Exercise

☐ Call someone   ☐ ....

'On awakening let us think about the twenty-four hours ahead...'

6 am
7 am
8 am
9 am
10 am
11 am
12 pm
1 pm
2 pm
3 pm
4 pm
5 pm
6 pm
7 pm
8 pm
9 pm

'A genuine gratitude for blessings received'

_____
_____
_____
_____
_____

'God, grant me the serenity to accept the things I cannot change'

_____
_____
_____
_____

- ☐ Prayer & meditation
- ☐ Service/help someone
- ☐ Spiritual reading
- ☐ Exercise
- ☐ Call someone
- ☐ ....

'...We consider our plans for the day'

6 am

7 am

8 am

9 am

10 am

11 am

12 pm

1 pm

2 pm

3 pm

4 pm

5 pm

6 pm

7 pm

8 pm

9 pm

Date: _____   Sobriety Tracker: _____

journal

How can I be more loving towards the people in my life?

_____
_____
_____
_____
_____
_____
_____
_____
_____
_____
_____
_____
_____

personal inventory

'When we retire at night, we constructively review our day'

Was I unkind (cruel, harsh, unfeeling)?

Who did I help today?

How did I show love to myself? Did I talk negatively to myself?

Am I obsessing about anything?

What am I proud of today?

Was I patient, kind and compassionate? What caused me to lose these attitudes? Do I owe anyone amends?

journal

How can I contribute more to the wellbeing of others?

personal inventory

'When we retire at night, we constructively review our day'

Was I resentful, selfish, dishonest or afraid?

Do I owe an apology?

Have I kept something to myself which should be discussed with another person at once?

Was I kind and loving towards all?

What could I have done better?

Was I thinking about myself most of the time? Or was I thinking of what I could do for others, of what I could pack into the stream of life?

I'm grateful for...

today I accept...

- ☐ Prayer & meditation
- ☐ Service/help someone
- ☐ Spiritual reading
- ☐ Exercise
- ☐ Call someone
- ☐ ....

'On awakening let us think about the twenty-four hours ahead...'

6 am
7 am
8 am
9 am
10 am
11 am
12 pm
1 pm
2 pm
3 pm
4 pm
5 pm
6 pm
7 pm
8 pm
9 pm

Weekly Check-in

Review of the week

- [ ] Review My Triggers
- [ ] Review My Rescue Plan
- [ ] Review People to stay in touch with
- [ ] Complete Spiritual Planner

What's working and why is it working?

What part of my recovery have I been neglecting?

What do I need to pay more attention to?

Have I had fun this week? How can I have more fun?

Spiritual Planner

My 2 main spiritual/recovery priorities for this week:

1.

2.

Spiritual and recovery-based activities for the week:

monday

tuesday

wednesday

thursday

friday

saturday

sunday

Date: _____   Sobriety Tracker: _____

journal

> What fears do I have at the moment?

_____
_____
_____
_____
_____
_____
_____
_____
_____
_____
_____
_____

I'm grateful for...

_____
_____
_____
_____

today I accept...

_____
_____

☐ Prayer & meditation   ☐ Service/help someone

☐ Spiritual reading   ☐ Exercise

☐ Call someone   ☐ ....

'On awakening let us think about the twenty-four hours ahead...'

6 am
7 am
8 am
9 am
10 am
11 am
12 pm
1 pm
2 pm
3 pm
4 pm
5 pm
6 pm
7 pm
8 pm
9 pm

personal inventory

'When we retire at night, we constructively review our day'

Was I resentful, selfish, dishonest or afraid?
_____

Do I owe an apology?
_____

Have I kept something to myself which should be discussed with another person at once?
_____

Was I kind and loving towards all?
_____

What could I have done better?
_____

Was I thinking about myself most of the time? Or was I thinking of what I could do for others, of what I could pack into the stream of life?
_____

'A genuine gratitude for blessings received'

....
....
....
....

'God, grant me the serenity to accept the things I cannot change'

....
....
....

- ☐ Prayer & meditation
- ☐ Service/help someone
- ☐ Spiritual reading
- ☐ Exercise
- ☐ Call someone
- ☐ ....

'...We consider our plans for the day'

	6 am
	7 am
	8 am
	9 am
	10 am
	11 am
	12 pm
	1 pm
	2 pm
	3 pm
	4 pm
	5 pm
	6 pm
	7 pm
	8 pm
	9 pm

Date: ....   Sobriety Tracker: ....

journal

> Was there a turning point in my life?

....
....
....
....
....
....
....
....
....
....
....
....
....
....
....
....

personal inventory

'When we retire at night, we constructively review our day'

Did I do something for someone else today?

What did I accomplish today?

What have I done for my recovery today?

Am I taking care of my body?

What could I have done better?

Was I unloving today (cold, unresponsive, indifferent)?

Date: _____   Sobriety Tracker: _____

journal

What am I feeling right now?

_____
_____
_____
_____
_____
_____
_____
_____
_____
_____
_____
_____
_____

personal inventory

'When we retire at night, we constructively review our day'

Was I resentful, selfish, dishonest or afraid?	
Do I owe an apology?	
Have I kept something to myself which should be discussed with another person at once?	
Was I kind and loving towards all?	
What could I have done better?	
Was I thinking about myself most of the time? Or was I thinking of what I could do for others, of what I could pack into the stream of life?	

I'm grateful for...

_____
_____
_____

today I accept...

_____
_____

☐ Prayer & meditation   ☐ Service/help someone

☐ Spiritual reading   ☐ Exercise

☐ Call someone   ☐ ....

'On awakening let us think about the twenty-four hours ahead...'

6 am
7 am
8 am
9 am
10 am
11 am
12 pm
1 pm
2 pm
3 pm
4 pm
5 pm
6 pm
7 pm
8 pm
9 pm

'A genuine gratitude for blessings received'

....
....
....
....

'God, grant me the serenity to accept the things I cannot change'

....
....
....
....

journal

> How can I be more helpful to those around me?

☐ Prayer & meditation   ☐ Service/help someone

☐ Spiritual reading   ☐ Exercise

☐ Call someone   ☐ ....

'...We consider our plans for the day'

	6 am
	7 am
	8 am
	9 am
	10 am
	11 am
	12 pm
	1 pm
	2 pm
	3 pm
	4 pm
	5 pm
	6 pm
	7 pm
	8 pm
	9 pm

....
....
....
....
....
....
....
....
....
....
....
....
....

personal inventory

'When we retire at night, we constructively review our day'

Was I honest with others and myself today?

What can I celebrate? What could I have done differently?

How was my serenity? Did anything happen that caused me to lose it? What was my part in it?

Am I spending time on myself?

What did I do to connect with my higher power?

Did fear prevent me from doing anything today?

journal

> What new hobby or sport would I like to start?

I'm grateful for...

today I accept...

- [ ] Prayer & meditation
- [ ] Spiritual reading
- [ ] Call someone
- [ ] Service/help someone
- [ ] Exercise
- [ ] ....

personal inventory

'When we retire at night, we constructively review our day'

Was I resentful, selfish, dishonest or afraid?	
Do I owe an apology?	
Have I kept something to myself which should be discussed with another person at once?	
Was I kind and loving towards all?	
What could I have done better?	
Was I thinking about myself most of the time? Or was I thinking of what I could do for others, of what I could pack into the stream of life?	

'On awakening let us think about the twenty-four hours ahead...'

6 am
7 am
8 am
9 am
10 am
11 am
12 pm
1 pm
2 pm
3 pm
4 pm
5 pm
6 pm
7 pm
8 pm
9 pm

'A genuine gratitude for blessings received'

_____

_____

_____

_____

'God, grant me the serenity to accept the things I cannot change'

_____

_____

_____

- ☐ Prayer & meditation
- ☐ Service/help someone
- ☐ Spiritual reading
- ☐ Exercise
- ☐ Call someone
- ☐ ....

'...We consider our plans for the day'

	6 am
	7 am
	8 am
	9 am
	10 am
	11 am
	12 pm
	1 pm
	2 pm
	3 pm
	4 pm
	5 pm
	6 pm
	7 pm
	8 pm
	9 pm

journal

What period of my life did I like the most? Why?

_____

_____

_____

_____

_____

_____

_____

_____

_____

_____

_____

_____

personal inventory

'When we retire at night, we constructively review our day'

Have I practiced any of my character defects?

Am I keeping any secrets?

Was I honest? Did I keep my word with everyone? Did I keep my word with myself?

Am I trying to fill the void with external stimuli?

Did I learn something useful today? Or was I a mental loafer?

Was I concerned today with thoughts or behaviours linked to my addiction?

Date: _____ Sobriety Tracker: _____

journal

Do I say 'yes' or 'no' more often?

_____
_____
_____
_____
_____
_____
_____
_____
_____
_____
_____
_____
_____
_____

personal inventory

'When we retire at night, we constructively review our day'

Was I resentful, selfish, dishonest or afraid?
_____

Do I owe an apology?
_____

Have I kept something to myself which should be discussed with another person at once?
_____

Was I kind and loving towards all?
_____

What could I have done better?
_____

Was I thinking about myself most of the time? Or was I thinking of what I could do for others, of what I could pack into the stream of life?
_____

I'm grateful for…

_____
_____
_____

today I accept…

_____
_____
_____

☐ Prayer & meditation   ☐ Service/help someone

☐ Spiritual reading   ☐ Exercise

☐ Call someone   ☐ _____

'On awakening let us think about the twenty-four hours ahead…'

6 am	
7 am	
8 am	
9 am	
10 am	
11 am	
12 pm	
1 pm	
2 pm	
3 pm	
4 pm	
5 pm	
6 pm	
7 pm	
8 pm	
9 pm	

Weekly Check-in

Review of the week

- [ ] Review What would happen if I relapse
- [ ] Review My Character Defects
- [ ] Review People to stay in touch with
- [ ] Complete Spiritual Planner

What's made me happy this week?

What's been most difficult this week? Do I need to change something?

What do I need to start doing? What do I need to stop doing?

How can I prioritise my time better?

Spiritual Planner

My 2 main spiritual/recovery priorities for this week:

1.

2.

Spiritual and recovery-based activities for the week:

monday

tuesday

wednesday

thursday

friday

saturday

sunday

Date: _____   Sobriety Tracker: _____

journal

> What have I been putting off that I really should face?

_____
_____
_____
_____
_____
_____
_____
_____
_____
_____
_____
_____
_____

personal inventory

'When we retire at night, we constructively review our day'

Was I resentful, selfish, dishonest or afraid?	
Do I owe an apology?	
Have I kept something to myself which should be discussed with another person at once?	
Was I kind and loving towards all?	
What could I have done better?	
Was I thinking about myself most of the time? Or was I thinking of what I could do for others, of what I could pack into the stream of life?	

I'm grateful for...

_____
_____
_____
_____

today I accept...

_____
_____

☐ Prayer & meditation   ☐ Service/help someone

☐ Spiritual reading   ☐ Exercise

☐ Call someone   ☐ ....

'On awakening let us think about the twenty-four hours ahead...'

6 am	
7 am	
8 am	
9 am	
10 am	
11 am	
12 pm	
1 pm	
2 pm	
3 pm	
4 pm	
5 pm	
6 pm	
7 pm	
8 pm	
9 pm	

'A genuine gratitude for blessings received'

_____
_____
_____
_____
_____

'God, grant me the serenity to accept the
things I cannot change'

_____
_____
_____
_____

- ☐ Prayer & meditation
- ☐ Service/help someone
- ☐ Spiritual reading
- ☐ Exercise
- ☐ Call someone
- ☐ ....

'...We consider our plans for the day'

	6 am
	7 am
	8 am
	9 am
	10 am
	11 am
	12 pm
	1 pm
	2 pm
	3 pm
	4 pm
	5 pm
	6 pm
	7 pm
	8 pm
	9 pm

Date: _____   Sobriety Tracker: _____

journal

After prayer and meditation, what am I inspired to do today?

_____
_____
_____
_____
_____
_____
_____
_____
_____
_____
_____
_____

personal inventory

'When we retire at night, we constructively review our day'

How did I take care of my health (physical, emotional, spiritual) today?
_____
_____
_____

What have I enjoyed about today?
_____
_____

How did I show love to others? Did I act unlovingly towards anyone?
_____
_____
_____

Who neds my prayers today?
_____
_____

Am I holding any resentments?
_____
_____

How is my spiritual condition?
_____
_____

Date: _____ Sobriety Tracker: _____

journal

How open am I with others?

_____
_____
_____
_____
_____
_____
_____
_____
_____
_____
_____
_____
_____
_____
_____

personal inventory

'When we retire at night, we constructively review our day'

Was I resentful, selfish, dishonest or afraid?	
Do I owe an apology?	
Have I kept something to myself which should be discussed with another person at once?	
Was I kind and loving towards all?	
What could I have done better?	
Was I thinking about myself most of the time? Or was I thinking of what I could do for others, of what I could pack into the stream of life?	

I'm grateful for...

_____
_____
_____
_____

today I accept...

_____
_____
_____

☐ Prayer & meditation   ☐ Service/help someone

☐ Spiritual reading   ☐ Exercise

☐ Call someone   ☐ _____

'On awakening let us think about the twenty-four hours ahead...'

6 am	
7 am	
8 am	
9 am	
10 am	
11 am	
12 pm	
1 pm	
2 pm	
3 pm	
4 pm	
5 pm	
6 pm	
7 pm	
8 pm	
9 pm	

'A genuine gratitude for blessings received'

....
....
....
....

'God, grant me the serenity to accept the things I cannot change'

....
....
....
....

- ☐ Prayer & meditation
- ☐ Service/help someone
- ☐ Spiritual reading
- ☐ Exercise
- ☐ Call someone
- ☐ ....

'...We consider our plans for the day'

	6 am
	7 am
	8 am
	9 am
	10 am
	11 am
	12 pm
	1 pm
	2 pm
	3 pm
	4 pm
	5 pm
	6 pm
	7 pm
	8 pm
	9 pm

Date: ....   Sobriety Tracker: ....

journal

> What's my favourite time of day? Why?

....
....
....
....
....
....
....
....
....
....
....
....
....
....
....

personal inventory

'When we retire at night, we constructively review our day'

Was I unkind (cruel, harsh, unfeeling)?

Who did I help today?

How did I show love to myself? Did I talk negatively to myself?

Am I obsessing about anything?

What am I proud of today?

Was I patient, kind and compassionate? What caused me to lose these attitudes? Do I owe anyone amends?

Date: _____ Sobriety Tracker: _____

journal

How do I want to be today?

_____
_____
_____
_____
_____
_____
_____
_____
_____
_____
_____
_____
_____

I'm grateful for...

_____
_____
_____

today I accept...

_____
_____

- ☐ Prayer & meditation
- ☐ Service/help someone
- ☐ Spiritual reading
- ☐ Exercise
- ☐ Call someone
- ☐ ....

personal inventory

'When we retire at night, we constructively review our day'

Was I resentful, selfish, dishonest or afraid?
_____

Do I owe an apology?
_____

Have I kept something to myself which should be discussed with another person at once?
_____

Was I kind and loving towards all?
_____

What could I have done better?
_____

Was I thinking about myself most of the time? Or was I thinking of what I could do for others, of what I could pack into the stream of life?
_____

'On awakening let us think about the twenty-four hours ahead...'

6 am
7 am
8 am
9 am
10 am
11 am
12 pm
1 pm
2 pm
3 pm
4 pm
5 pm
6 pm
7 pm
8 pm
9 pm

'A genuine gratitude for blessings received'

....

....

....

....

'God, grant me the serenity to accept the things I cannot change'

....

....

....

....

- ☐ Prayer & meditation
- ☐ Service/help someone
- ☐ Spiritual reading
- ☐ Exercise
- ☐ Call someone
- ☐ ....

'...We consider our plans for the day'

	6 am
	7 am
	8 am
	9 am
	10 am
	11 am
	12 pm
	1 pm
	2 pm
	3 pm
	4 pm
	5 pm
	6 pm
	7 pm
	8 pm
	9 pm

Date: ....

Sobriety Tracker: ....

journal

How can I take better care of my body?

personal inventory

'When we retire at night, we constructively review our day'

Did I do something for someone else today?

What did I accomplish today?

What have I done for my recovery today?

Am I taking care of my body?

What could I have done better?

Was I unloving today (cold, unresponsive, indifferent)?

Date: _____ Sobriety Tracker: _____

journal

Who are the most important people in my life? Why?

_____
_____
_____
_____
_____
_____
_____
_____
_____
_____
_____
_____
_____
_____

personal inventory

'When we retire at night, we constructively review our day'

Was I resentful, selfish, dishonest or afraid?
_____

Do I owe an apology?
_____

Have I kept something to myself which should be discussed with another person at once?
_____

Was I kind and loving towards all?
_____

What could I have done better?
_____

Was I thinking about myself most of the time? Or was I thinking of what I could do for others, of what I could pack into the stream of life?
_____

I'm grateful for...
_____
_____
_____

today I accept...
_____
_____

- [ ] Prayer & meditation
- [ ] Service/help someone
- [ ] Spiritual reading
- [ ] Exercise
- [ ] Call someone
- [ ] ....

'On awakening let us think about the twenty-four hours ahead...'

6 am
7 am
8 am
9 am
10 am
11 am
12 pm
1 pm
2 pm
3 pm
4 pm
5 pm
6 pm
7 pm
8 pm
9 pm

Weekly Check-in

Review of the week

> ☐ Review My vision for the future
>
> ☐ Review My Rescue Plan
>
> ☐ Review People to stay in touch with
>
> ☐ Complete Spiritual Planner

What's been the biggest positive this week?

What fears have been holding me back?

Do I need to ask for some help next week? Is there anyone who needs my help?

Have I been looking after myself this week?

Spiritual Planner

My 2 main spiritual/recovery priorities for this week:

1.

2.

Spiritual and recovery-based activities for the week:

monday

tuesday

wednesday

thursday

friday

saturday

sunday

journal

> What things do I really value in my life?

_____
_____
_____
_____
_____
_____
_____
_____
_____
_____
_____
_____
_____
_____

personal inventory

'When we retire at night, we constructively review our day'

Was I resentful, selfish, dishonest or afraid?	
Do I owe an apology?	
Have I kept something to myself which should be discussed with another person at once?	
Was I kind and loving towards all?	
What could I have done better?	
Was I thinking about myself most of the time? Or was I thinking of what I could do for others, of what I could pack into the stream of life?	

I'm grateful for...

_____
_____
_____

today I accept...

_____
_____
_____

☐ Prayer & meditation   ☐ Service/help someone

☐ Spiritual reading   ☐ Exercise

☐ Call someone   ☐ ....

'On awakening let us think about the twenty-four hours ahead...'

6 am
7 am
8 am
9 am
10 am
11 am
12 pm
1 pm
2 pm
3 pm
4 pm
5 pm
6 pm
7 pm
8 pm
9 pm

'A genuine gratitude for blessings received'

....

....

*'God, grant me the serenity to accept the
things I cannot change'*

....

....

....

journal

How can I be less judgemental?

☐ Prayer & meditation   ☐ Service/help someone

☐ Spiritual reading   ☐ Exercise

☐ Call someone   ☐ ....

'...We consider our plans for the day'

6 am

7 am

8 am

9 am

10 am

11 am

12 pm

1 pm

2 pm

3 pm

4 pm

5 pm

6 pm

7 pm

8 pm

9 pm

personal inventory

'When we retire at night, we constructively review our day'

Was I honest with others and myself today?

What can I celebrate? What could I have done differently?

How was my serenity? Did anything happen that caused me to lose it? What was my part in it?

Am I spending time on myself?

What did I do to connect with my higher power?

Did fear prevent me from doing anything today?

Date: _____   Sobriety Tracker: _____

journal

> How can I avoid being a mental loafer today?

_____
_____
_____
_____
_____
_____
_____
_____
_____
_____
_____
_____
_____
_____
_____

personal inventory

'When we retire at night, we constructively review our day'

Was I resentful, selfish, dishonest or afraid?

Do I owe an apology?

Have I kept something to myself which should be discussed with another person at once?

Was I kind and loving towards all?

What could I have done better?

Was I thinking about myself most of the time? Or was I thinking of what I could do for others, of what I could pack into the stream of life?

I'm grateful for...

_____
_____
_____

today I accept...

_____
_____

☐ Prayer & meditation   ☐ Service/help someone

☐ Spiritual reading   ☐ Exercise

☐ Call someone   ☐ _____

'On awakening let us think about the twenty-four hours ahead...'

6 am

7 am

8 am

9 am

10 am

11 am

12 pm

1 pm

2 pm

3 pm

4 pm

5 pm

6 pm

7 pm

8 pm

9 pm

'A genuine gratitude for blessings received'

....

....

....

....

*'God, grant me the serenity to accept the
things I cannot change'*

....

....

....

....

- [ ] Prayer & meditation
- [ ] Spiritual reading
- [ ] Call someone
- [ ] Service/help someone
- [ ] Exercise
- [ ] ....

'...We consider our plans for the day'

	6 am
	7 am
	8 am
	9 am
	10 am
	11 am
	12 pm
	1 pm
	2 pm
	3 pm
	4 pm
	5 pm
	6 pm
	7 pm
	8 pm
	9 pm

Date: _____   Sobriety Tracker: _____

journal

How am I spending the majority of my time?

....

....

....

....

....

....

....

....

....

....

....

....

personal inventory

'When we retire at night, we constructively review our day'

Have I practiced any of my character defects?

Am I keeping any secrets?

Was I honest? Did I keep my word with everyone? Did I keep my word with myself?

Am I trying to fill the void with external stimuli?

Did I learn something useful today? Or was I a mental loafer?

Was I concerned today with thoughts or behaviours linked to my addiction?

Date: _____   Sobriety Tracker: _____

journal

> What qualities do I wish to develop?

....
....
....
....
....
....
....
....
....
....
....
....
....

personal inventory

'When we retire at night, we constructively review our day'

Was I resentful, selfish, dishonest or afraid?
....
....

Do I owe an apology?
....
....

Have I kept something to myself which should be discussed with another person at once?
....
....
....
....

Was I kind and loving towards all?
....
....

What could I have done better?
....
....

Was I thinking about myself most of the time? Or was I thinking of what I could do for others, of what I could pack into the stream of life?
....
....
....
....

I'm grateful for...
....
....
....
....

today I accept...
....
....
....

☐ Prayer & meditation   ☐ Service/help someone

☐ Spiritual reading   ☐ Exercise

☐ Call someone   ☐ ....

'On awakening let us think about the twenty-four hours ahead...'

6 am	
7 am	
8 am	
9 am	
10 am	
11 am	
12 pm	
1 pm	
2 pm	
3 pm	
4 pm	
5 pm	
6 pm	
7 pm	
8 pm	
9 pm	

'A genuine gratitude for blessings received'

....
....
....

'God, grant me the serenity to accept the things I cannot change'

....
....

☐ Prayer & meditation ☐ Service/help someone

☐ Spiritual reading ☐ Exercise

☐ Call someone ☐ ....

'...We consider our plans for the day'

6 am

7 am

8 am

9 am

10 am

11 am

12 pm

1 pm

2 pm

3 pm

4 pm

5 pm

6 pm

7 pm

8 pm

9 pm

journal

What can I do or create that brings me inner peace and joy?

personal inventory

'When we retire at night, we constructively review our day'

How did I take care of my health (physical, emotional, spiritual) today?

What have I enjoyed about today?

How did I show love to others? Did I act unlovingly towards anyone?

Who neds my prayers today?

Am I holding any resentments?

How is my spiritual condition?

journal

What small changes to my lifestyle can I make that would positively impact the world?

I'm grateful for...

today I accept...

☐ Prayer & meditation   ☐ Service/help someone

☐ Spiritual reading   ☐ Exercise

☐ Call someone   ☐

'On awakening let us think about the twenty-four hours ahead...'

6 am
7 am
8 am
9 am
10 am
11 am
12 pm
1 pm
2 pm
3 pm
4 pm
5 pm
6 pm
7 pm
8 pm
9 pm

personal inventory

'When we retire at night, we constructively review our day'

Was I resentful, selfish, dishonest or afraid?

Do I owe an apology?

Have I kept something to myself which should be discussed with another person at once?

Was I kind and loving towards all?

What could I have done better?

Was I thinking about myself most of the time? Or was I thinking of what I could do for others, of what I could pack into the stream of life?

Weekly Check-in

Review of the week

- [ ] Review How I'll know if I'm heading for a relapse
- [ ] Review My Character Defects
- [ ] Review People to stay in touch with
- [ ] Complete Spiritual Planner

What's gone well this week?

What are the biggest distractions in my life? How can I remove them?

Which part of the program do I need to prioritise next week?

How is my spiritual condition?

Spiritual Planner

My 2 main spiritual/recovery priorities for this week:

1.

2.

Spiritual and recovery-based activities for the week:

monday	
tuesday	
wednesday	
thursday	
friday	
saturday	
sunday	

Date: _____   Sobriety Tracker: _____

journal

How often do I procrastinate?

_____
_____
_____
_____
_____
_____
_____
_____
_____
_____
_____
_____
_____
_____
_____

personal inventory

'When we retire at night, we constructively review our day'

Was I resentful, selfish, dishonest or afraid?
_____
_____

Do I owe an apology?
_____

Have I kept something to myself which should be discussed with another person at once?
_____
_____
_____

Was I kind and loving towards all?
_____
_____

What could I have done better?
_____
_____

Was I thinking about myself most of the time? Or was I thinking of what I could do for others, of what I could pack into the stream of life?
_____
_____
_____

I'm grateful for...
_____
_____
_____
_____

today I accept...
_____
_____
_____

☐ Prayer & meditation   ☐ Service/help someone

☐ Spiritual reading   ☐ Exercise

☐ Call someone   ☐ ....

'On awakening let us think about the twenty-four hours ahead...'

6 am	
7 am	
8 am	
9 am	
10 am	
11 am	
12 pm	
1 pm	
2 pm	
3 pm	
4 pm	
5 pm	
6 pm	
7 pm	
8 pm	
9 pm	

'A genuine gratitude for blessings received'

_____
_____
_____
_____

'God, grant me the serenity to accept the things I cannot change'

_____
_____
_____

- [ ] Prayer & meditation
- [ ] Service/help someone
- [ ] Spiritual reading
- [ ] Exercise
- [ ] Call someone
- [ ] ....

'...We consider our plans for the day'

	6 am
	7 am
	8 am
	9 am
	10 am
	11 am
	12 pm
	1 pm
	2 pm
	3 pm
	4 pm
	5 pm
	6 pm
	7 pm
	8 pm
	9 pm

Date: _____ Sobriety Tracker: _____

journal

What's on my 'to-do' list that never gets done?

_____
_____
_____
_____
_____
_____
_____
_____
_____
_____
_____
_____
_____

personal inventory

'When we retire at night, we constructively review our day'

Was I unkind (cruel, harsh, unfeeling)?

Who did I help today?

How did I show love to myself? Did I talk negatively to myself?

Am I obsessing about anything?

What am I proud of today?

Was I patient, kind and compassionate? What caused me to lose these attitudes? Do I owe anyone amends?

Date: _____ Sobriety Tracker: _____

journal

> When's the last time I learned something new?

_____
_____
_____
_____
_____
_____
_____
_____
_____
_____
_____
_____
_____
_____
_____

personal inventory

'When we retire at night, we constructively review our day'

Was I resentful, selfish, dishonest or afraid?
_____

Do I owe an apology?
_____

Have I kept something to myself which should be discussed with another person at once?
_____

Was I kind and loving towards all?
_____

What could I have done better?
_____

Was I thinking about myself most of the time? Or was I thinking of what I could do for others, of what I could pack into the stream of life?
_____

I'm grateful for...

_____
_____
_____

today I accept...

_____
_____

☐ Prayer & meditation   ☐ Service/help someone

☐ Spiritual reading   ☐ Exercise

☐ Call someone   ☐ ....

'On awakening let us think about the twenty-four hours ahead...'

6 am
7 am
8 am
9 am
10 am
11 am
12 pm
1 pm
2 pm
3 pm
4 pm
5 pm
6 pm
7 pm
8 pm
9 pm

'A genuine gratitude for blessings received'

....

....

....

'God, grant me the serenity to accept the things I cannot change'

....

....

....

- ☐ Prayer & meditation
- ☐ Service/help someone
- ☐ Spiritual reading
- ☐ Exercise
- ☐ Call someone
- ☐ ....

'...We consider our plans for the day'

	6 am
	7 am
	8 am
	9 am
	10 am
	11 am
	12 pm
	1 pm
	2 pm
	3 pm
	4 pm
	5 pm
	6 pm
	7 pm
	8 pm
	9 pm

Date: _____   Sobriety Tracker: _____

journal

Do I have a relationship that needs mending?

....

....

....

....

....

....

....

....

....

....

....

....

....

....

personal inventory

'When we retire at night, we constructively review our day'

Did I do something for someone else today?

What did I accomplish today?

What have I done for my recovery today?

Am I taking care of my body?

What could I have done better?

Was I unloving today (cold, unresponsive, indifferent)?

Date: _____ Sobriety Tracker: _____

journal

> What is no longer acceptable in my life?

_____
_____
_____
_____
_____
_____
_____
_____
_____
_____
_____
_____
_____
_____

personal inventory

'When we retire at night, we constructively review our day'

Was I resentful, selfish, dishonest or afraid?

Do I owe an apology?

Have I kept something to myself which should be discussed with another person at once?

Was I kind and loving towards all?

What could I have done better?

Was I thinking about myself most of the time? Or was I thinking of what I could do for others, of what I could pack into the stream of life?

I'm grateful for...

_____
_____
_____
_____

today I accept...

_____
_____
_____

☐ Prayer & meditation   ☐ Service/help someone

☐ Spiritual reading   ☐ Exercise

☐ Call someone   ☐ ....

'On awakening let us think about the twenty-four hours ahead...'

6 am
7 am
8 am
9 am
10 am
11 am
12 pm
1 pm
2 pm
3 pm
4 pm
5 pm
6 pm
7 pm
8 pm
9 pm

'A genuine gratitude for blessings received'

....

....

....

'God, grant me the serenity to accept the things I cannot change'

....

....

....

....

☐ Prayer & meditation   ☐ Service/help someone

☐ Spiritual reading   ☐ Exercise

☐ Call someone   ☐ ....

'...We consider our plans for the day'

6 am

7 am

8 am

9 am

10 am

11 am

12 pm

1 pm

2 pm

3 pm

4 pm

5 pm

6 pm

7 pm

8 pm

9 pm

journal

Do I enjoy spending time alone?

....

....

....

....

....

....

....

....

....

....

....

....

....

personal inventory

'When we retire at night, we constructively review our day'

Was I honest with others and myself today?

What can I celebrate? What could I have done differently?

How was my serenity? Did anything happen that caused me to lose it? What was my part in it?

Am I spending time on myself?

What did I do to connect with my higher power?

Did fear prevent me from doing anything today?

Date: _____   Sobriety Tracker: _____

journal

| What stresses me out? |

....
....
....
....
....
....
....
....
....
....
....
....
....
....
....
....
....
....

personal inventory

'When we retire at night, we constructively review our day'

Was I resentful, selfish, dishonest or afraid?	....
Do I owe an apology?	....
Have I kept something to myself which should be discussed with another person at once?	....
Was I kind and loving towards all?	....
What could I have done better?	....
Was I thinking about myself most of the time? Or was I thinking of what I could do for others, of what I could pack into the stream of life?	....

I'm grateful for...

....
....
....

today I accept...

....
....

☐ Prayer & meditation   ☐ Service/help someone

☐ Spiritual reading   ☐ Exercise

☐ Call someone   ☐ ....

'On awakening let us think about the twenty-four hours ahead...'

6 am
7 am
8 am
9 am
10 am
11 am
12 pm
1 pm
2 pm
3 pm
4 pm
5 pm
6 pm
7 pm
8 pm
9 pm

Weekly Check-in

Review of the week

- [ ] Review My Rock Bottom
- [ ] Review My Character Defects
- [ ] Review People to stay in touch with
- [ ] Complete Spiritual Planner

What have I achieved this week?

What's not working? What am I willing to do about it?

What one thing can I do next week that will have the biggest positive impact on my life?

What do I need to make a decision about?

Spiritual Planner

My 2 main spiritual/recovery priorities for this week:

1.

2.

Spiritual and recovery-based activities for the week:

monday

tuesday

wednesday

thursday

friday

saturday

sunday

Date: _____   Sobriety Tracker: _____

journal

How do I currently feel about myself?

....
....
....
....
....
....
....
....
....
....
....
....
....

personal inventory

'When we retire at night, we constructively review our day'

Was I resentful, selfish, dishonest or afraid?
....
....

Do I owe an apology?
....
....

Have I kept something to myself which should be discussed with another person at once?
....
....
....
....

Was I kind and loving towards all?
....
....

What could I have done better?
....
....

Was I thinking about myself most of the time? Or was I thinking of what I could do for others, of what I could pack into the stream of life?
....
....
....
....
....

I'm grateful for...

....
....
....
....

today I accept...

....
....
....

☐ Prayer & meditation   ☐ Service/help someone

☐ Spiritual reading   ☐ Exercise

☐ Call someone   ☐ ....

'On awakening let us think about the twenty-four hours ahead...'

6 am
7 am
8 am
9 am
10 am
11 am
12 pm
1 pm
2 pm
3 pm
4 pm
5 pm
6 pm
7 pm
8 pm
9 pm

'A genuine gratitude for blessings received'

....
....
....
....

'God, grant me the serenity to accept the things I cannot change'

....
....
....

- ☐ Prayer & meditation
- ☐ Spiritual reading
- ☐ Call someone
- ☐ Service/help someone
- ☐ Exercise
- ☐ ....

'...We consider our plans for the day'

	6 am
	7 am
	8 am
	9 am
	10 am
	11 am
	12 pm
	1 pm
	2 pm
	3 pm
	4 pm
	5 pm
	6 pm
	7 pm
	8 pm
	9 pm

journal

What do I need to let go of?

....
....
....
....
....
....
....
....
....
....
....
....
....
....
....

personal inventory

'When we retire at night, we constructively review our day'

Have I practiced any of my character defects?

Am I keeping any secrets?

Was I honest? Did I keep my word with everyone? Did I keep my word with myself?

Am I trying to fill the void with external stimuli?

Did I learn something useful today? Or was I a mental loafer?

Was I concerned today with thoughts or behaviours linked to my addiction?

Date: _____ Sobriety Tracker: _____

journal

> What decisions do I need to make that I've been putting off?

....
....
....
....
....
....
....
....
....
....
....
....
....

personal inventory

'When we retire at night, we constructively review our day'

Was I resentful, selfish, dishonest or afraid?
....

Do I owe an apology?
....

Have I kept something to myself which should be discussed with another person at once?
....

Was I kind and loving towards all?
....

What could I have done better?
....

Was I thinking about myself most of the time? Or was I thinking of what I could do for others, of what I could pack into the stream of life?
....

I'm grateful for...

....
....
....

today I accept...

....
....
....

☐ Prayer & meditation   ☐ Service/help someone

☐ Spiritual reading   ☐ Exercise

☐ Call someone   ☐ ....

'On awakening let us think about the twenty-four hours ahead...'

6 am	
7 am	
8 am	
9 am	
10 am	
11 am	
12 pm	
1 pm	
2 pm	
3 pm	
4 pm	
5 pm	
6 pm	
7 pm	
8 pm	
9 pm	

'A genuine gratitude for blessings received'

_____
_____
_____
_____

'God, grant me the serenity to accept the things I cannot change'

_____
_____
_____
_____

☐ Prayer & meditation   ☐ Service/help someone

☐ Spiritual reading   ☐ Exercise

☐ Call someone   ☐ ....

'...We consider our plans for the day'

	6 am
	7 am
	8 am
	9 am
	10 am
	11 am
	12 pm
	1 pm
	2 pm
	3 pm
	4 pm
	5 pm
	6 pm
	7 pm
	8 pm
	9 pm

journal

> Do I need to be more open-minded and accepting?

personal inventory

'When we retire at night, we constructively review our day'

How did I take care of my health (physical, emotional, spiritual) today?

What have I enjoyed about today?

How did I show love to others? Did I act unlovingly towards anyone?

Who neds my prayers today?

Am I holding any resentments?

How is my spiritual condition?

Date: _____ Sobriety Tracker: _____

journal

> Do I have healthy fun, or is it destructive?

_____
_____
_____
_____
_____
_____
_____
_____
_____
_____
_____
_____
_____
_____
_____

personal inventory

'When we retire at night, we constructively review our day'

Was I resentful, selfish, dishonest or afraid?	
Do I owe an apology?	
Have I kept something to myself which should be discussed with another person at once?	
Was I kind and loving towards all?	
What could I have done better?	
Was I thinking about myself most of the time? Or was I thinking of what I could do for others, of what I could pack into the stream of life?	

I'm grateful for...

_____
_____
_____
_____

today I accept...

_____
_____

☐ Prayer & meditation   ☐ Service/help someone

☐ Spiritual reading   ☐ Exercise

☐ Call someone   ☐ ....

'On awakening let us think about the twenty-four hours ahead...'

6 am	
7 am	
8 am	
9 am	
10 am	
11 am	
12 pm	
1 pm	
2 pm	
3 pm	
4 pm	
5 pm	
6 pm	
7 pm	
8 pm	
9 pm	

'A genuine gratitude for blessings received'

....
....
....
....

'God, grant me the serenity to accept the things I cannot change'

....
....
....
....

☐ Prayer & meditation ☐ Service/help someone

☐ Spiritual reading ☐ Exercise

☐ Call someone ☐ ....

'...We consider our plans for the day'

	6 am
	7 am
	8 am
	9 am
	10 am
	11 am
	12 pm
	1 pm
	2 pm
	3 pm
	4 pm
	5 pm
	6 pm
	7 pm
	8 pm
	9 pm

Date: _____   Sobriety Tracker: _____

journal

Where is my favourite place to be? Why?

....
....
....
....
....
....
....
....
....
....
....
....
....
....
....
....

personal inventory

'When we retire at night, we constructively review our day'

Was I unkind (cruel, harsh, unfeeling)?

Who did I help today?

How did I show love to myself? Did I talk negatively to myself?

Am I obsessing about anything?

What am I proud of today?

Was I patient, kind and compassionate? What caused me to lose these attitudes? Do I owe anyone amends?

journal

When did I last make a new friend?

I'm grateful for...

today I accept...

☐ Prayer & meditation

☐ Spiritual reading

☐ Call someone

☐ Service/help someone

☐ Exercise

☐ ....

personal inventory

'When we retire at night, we constructively review our day'

Was I resentful, selfish, dishonest or afraid?

Do I owe an apology?

Have I kept something to myself which should be discussed with another person at once?

Was I kind and loving towards all?

What could I have done better?

Was I thinking about myself most of the time? Or was I thinking of what I could do for others, of what I could pack into the stream of life?

'On awakening let us think about the twenty-four hours ahead...'

6 am

7 am

8 am

9 am

10 am

11 am

12 pm

1 pm

2 pm

3 pm

4 pm

5 pm

6 pm

7 pm

8 pm

9 pm

Weekly Check-in

Review of the week

- [ ] Review My Triggers
- [ ] Review My Rescue Plan
- [ ] Review People to stay in touch with
- [ ] Complete Spiritual Planner

What's working and why is it working?

What part of my recovery have I been neglecting?

What do I need to pay more attention to?

Have I had fun this week? How can I have more fun?

Spiritual Planner

My 2 main spiritual/recovery priorities for this week:

1.

2.

Spiritual and recovery-based activities for the week:

monday

tuesday

wednesday

thursday

friday

saturday

sunday

God, I turn my will and my life over to You this day for Your keeping. Your will, Lord, not mine. I ask for Your guidance and direction. I will walk humbly with You and Your fellowman. You are giving me a grateful heart for my many blessings. You are removing the defects of character that stand in my way. You are giving me freedom from self-will.

Let love, compassion, and understanding be in my every thought, word and deed this day. I release those to You who have mistreated me. I truly desire Your abundance of truth, love, harmony, and peace. As I go out today to do Your bidding, let me help anyone I can who is less fortunate than I.

My Daily Prayer

Bill P. and Lisa D. *The 12 Step Prayer Book. 2nd ed.* Center City, Minn.: Hazelden, 2004

Date: _____   Sobriety Tracker: _____

journal

How can I be a better father/mother/sister/brother/son/daughter?

....
....
....
....
....
....
....
....
....
....
....
....
....
....
....

personal inventory

'When we retire at night, we constructively review our day'

Was I resentful, selfish, dishonest or afraid?	....
Do I owe an apology?	....
Have I kept something to myself which should be discussed with another person at once?	....
Was I kind and loving towards all?	....
What could I have done better?	....
Was I thinking about myself most of the time? Or was I thinking of what I could do for others, of what I could pack into the stream of life?	....

I'm grateful for...

....
....
....

today I accept...

....
....

- ☐ Prayer & meditation
- ☐ Service/help someone
- ☐ Spiritual reading
- ☐ Exercise
- ☐ Call someone
- ☐ ....

'On awakening let us think about the twenty-four hours ahead...'

6 am
7 am
8 am
9 am
10 am
11 am
12 pm
1 pm
2 pm
3 pm
4 pm
5 pm
6 pm
7 pm
8 pm
9 pm

'A genuine gratitude for blessings received'

....

....

....

'God, grant me the serenity to accept the things I cannot change'

....

....

....

- ☐ Prayer & meditation
- ☐ Spiritual reading
- ☐ Call someone
- ☐ Service/help someone
- ☐ Exercise
- ☐ ....

'...We consider our plans for the day'

	6 am
	7 am
	8 am
	9 am
	10 am
	11 am
	12 pm
	1 pm
	2 pm
	3 pm
	4 pm
	5 pm
	6 pm
	7 pm
	8 pm
	9 pm

Date: _____   Sobriety Tracker: _____

journal

What makes me tired?
What gives me energy?

....

....

....

....

....

....

....

....

....

....

....

....

....

personal inventory

'When we retire at night, we constructively review our day'

Did I do something for someone else today?

....

What did I accomplish today?

....

What have I done for my recovery today?

....

Am I taking care of my body?

....

What could I have done better?

....

Was I unloving today (cold, unresponsive, indifferent)?

....

Date: _____ Sobriety Tracker: _____

journal

What makes me happy?

_____
_____
_____
_____
_____
_____
_____
_____
_____
_____
_____
_____
_____

personal inventory

'When we retire at night, we constructively review our day'

Was I resentful, selfish, dishonest or afraid?
_____
_____

Do I owe an apology?
_____
_____

Have I kept something to myself which should be discussed with another person at once?
_____
_____
_____

Was I kind and loving towards all?
_____
_____

What could I have done better?
_____
_____

Was I thinking about myself most of the time? Or was I thinking of what I could do for others, of what I could pack into the stream of life?
_____
_____
_____
_____

I'm grateful for...

_____
_____
_____
_____

today I accept...

_____
_____
_____

☐ Prayer & meditation   ☐ Service/help someone

☐ Spiritual reading   ☐ Exercise

☐ Call someone   ☐ _____

'On awakening let us think about the twenty-four hours ahead...'

6 am
7 am
8 am
9 am
10 am
11 am
12 pm
1 pm
2 pm
3 pm
4 pm
5 pm
6 pm
7 pm
8 pm
9 pm

'A genuine gratitude for blessings received'

_____
_____
_____
_____

'God, grant me the serenity to accept the things I cannot change'

_____
_____
_____

☐ Prayer & meditation   ☐ Service/help someone

☐ Spiritual reading   ☐ Exercise

☐ Call someone   ☐ ....

'...We consider our plans for the day'

	6 am
	7 am
	8 am
	9 am
	10 am
	11 am
	12 pm
	1 pm
	2 pm
	3 pm
	4 pm
	5 pm
	6 pm
	7 pm
	8 pm
	9 pm

Date: _____ Sobriety Tracker: _____

journal

How can I deepen my relationship with my higher power?

_____
_____
_____
_____
_____
_____
_____
_____
_____
_____
_____
_____
_____
_____
_____

personal inventory

'When we retire at night, we constructively review our day'

Was I honest with others and myself today?

What can I celebrate? What could I have done differently?

How was my serenity? Did anything happen that caused me to lose it? What was my part in it?

Am I spending time on myself?

What did I do to connect with my higher power?

Did fear prevent me from doing anything today?

Date: _____   Sobriety Tracker: _____

journal

> Am I good at handling change?
> How does it make me feel?

_____
_____
_____
_____
_____
_____
_____
_____
_____
_____
_____
_____
_____
_____

personal inventory

'When we retire at night, we constructively review our day'

Was I resentful, selfish, dishonest or afraid?
....
....

Do I owe an apology?
....
....

Have I kept something to myself which should be discussed with another person at once?
....
....
....
....

Was I kind and loving towards all?
....
....

What could I have done better?
....
....

Was I thinking about myself most of the time? Or was I thinking of what I could do for others, of what I could pack into the stream of life?
....
....
....
....
....
....

I'm grateful for...

....
....
....
....

today I accept...

....
....
....

☐ Prayer & meditation   ☐ Service/help someone

☐ Spiritual reading   ☐ Exercise

☐ Call someone   ☐ ....

'On awakening let us think about the twenty-four hours ahead...'

6 am
7 am
8 am
9 am
10 am
11 am
12 pm
1 pm
2 pm
3 pm
4 pm
5 pm
6 pm
7 pm
8 pm
9 pm

'A genuine gratitude for blessings received'

....
....
....
....

'God, grant me the serenity to accept the things I cannot change'

....
....
....

☐ Prayer & meditation   ☐ Service/help someone

☐ Spiritual reading   ☐ Exercise

☐ Call someone   ☐ ....

'...We consider our plans for the day'

6 am
7 am
8 am
9 am
10 am
11 am
12 pm
1 pm
2 pm
3 pm
4 pm
5 pm
6 pm
7 pm
8 pm
9 pm

journal

Do I need to listen more to those in my life?

....
....
....
....
....
....
....
....
....
....
....
....
....
....

personal inventory

'When we retire at night, we constructively review our day'

Have I practiced any of my character defects?

Am I keeping any secrets?

Was I honest? Did I keep my word with everyone? Did I keep my word with myself?

Am I trying to fill the void with external stimuli?

Did I learn something useful today? Or was I a mental loafer?

Was I concerned today with thoughts or behaviours linked to my addiction?

Date: _____ Sobriety Tracker: _____

journal

What's one of the most important things I learnt from my parents?

_____
_____
_____
_____
_____
_____
_____
_____
_____
_____
_____
_____
_____
_____
_____
_____

personal inventory

'When we retire at night, we constructively review our day'

Was I resentful, selfish, dishonest or afraid?
_____
_____

Do I owe an apology?
_____
_____

Have I kept something to myself which should be discussed with another person at once?
_____
_____
_____

Was I kind and loving towards all?
_____
_____

What could I have done better?
_____
_____

Was I thinking about myself most of the time? Or was I thinking of what I could do for others, of what I could pack into the stream of life?
_____
_____
_____
_____

I'm grateful for...
_____
_____ .
_____

today I accept...
_____
_____

☐ Prayer & meditation   ☐ Service/help someone

☐ Spiritual reading   ☐ Exercise

☐ Call someone   ☐ ....

'On awakening let us think about the twenty-four hours ahead...'

6 am
7 am
8 am
9 am
10 am
11 am
12 pm
1 pm
2 pm
3 pm
4 pm
5 pm
6 pm
7 pm
8 pm
9 pm

Weekly Check-in

Review of the week

- ☐ Review What would happen if I relapse
- ☐ Review My Character Defects
- ☐ Review People to stay in touch with
- ☐ Complete Spiritual Planner

What's made me happy this week?

What's been most difficult this week? Do I need to change something?

What do I need to start doing? What do I need to stop doing?

How can I prioritise my time better?

Spiritual Planner

My 2 main spiritual/recovery priorities for this week:

1.

2.

Spiritual and recovery-based activities for the week:

monday

tuesday

wednesday

thursday

friday

saturday

sunday

journal

Am I engaging in activities to escape reality?

personal inventory

'When we retire at night, we constructively review our day'

Was I resentful, selfish, dishonest or afraid?

Do I owe an apology?

Have I kept something to myself which should be discussed with another person at once?

Was I kind and loving towards all?

What could I have done better?

Was I thinking about myself most of the time? Or was I thinking of what I could do for others, of what I could pack into the stream of life?

I'm grateful for...

today I accept...

- ☐ Prayer & meditation
- ☐ Service/help someone
- ☐ Spiritual reading
- ☐ Exercise
- ☐ Call someone
- ☐ _____

'On awakening let us think about the twenty-four hours ahead...'

6 am

7 am

8 am

9 am

10 am

11 am

12 pm

1 pm

2 pm

3 pm

4 pm

5 pm

6 pm

7 pm

8 pm

9 pm

'A genuine gratitude for blessings received'

....
....
....
....

'God, grant me the serenity to accept the things I cannot change'

....
....
....
....

☐ Prayer & meditation   ☐ Service/help someone

☐ Spiritual reading   ☐ Exercise

☐ Call someone   ☐ ....

'...We consider our plans for the day'

	6 am
	7 am
	8 am
	9 am
	10 am
	11 am
	12 pm
	1 pm
	2 pm
	3 pm
	4 pm
	5 pm
	6 pm
	7 pm
	8 pm
	9 pm

journal

What scares me?

....
....
....
....
....
....
....
....
....
....
....
....
....
....
....
....

personal inventory

'When we retire at night, we constructively review our day'

How did I take care of my health (physical, emotional, spiritual) today?
....
....
....
....

What have I enjoyed about today?
....
....
....

How did I show love to others? Did I act unlovingly towards anyone?
....
....
....
....

Who neds my prayers today?
....
....

Am I holding any resentments?
....
....

How is my spiritual condition?
....
....

journal

Who needs my love today?
Who needs my prayers?

I'm grateful for...

today I accept...

- [ ] Prayer & meditation
- [ ] Spiritual reading
- [ ] Call someone
- [ ] Service/help someone
- [ ] Exercise
- [ ] ....

'On awakening let us think about the twenty-four hours ahead...'

6 am

7 am

8 am

9 am

10 am

11 am

12 pm

1 pm

2 pm

3 pm

4 pm

5 pm

6 pm

7 pm

8 pm

9 pm

personal inventory

'When we retire at night, we constructively review our day'

Was I resentful, selfish, dishonest or afraid?

Do I owe an apology?

Have I kept something to myself which should be discussed with another person at once?

Was I kind and loving towards all?

What could I have done better?

Was I thinking about myself most of the time? Or was I thinking of what I could do for others, of what I could pack into the stream of life?

'A genuine gratitude for blessings received'

....

....

....

....

'God, grant me the serenity to accept the things I cannot change'

....

....

....

....

- ☐ Prayer & meditation
- ☐ Service/help someone
- ☐ Spiritual reading
- ☐ Exercise
- ☐ Call someone
- ☐ ....

'...We consider our plans for the day'

	6 am
	7 am
	8 am
	9 am
	10 am
	11 am
	12 pm
	1 pm
	2 pm
	3 pm
	4 pm
	5 pm
	6 pm
	7 pm
	8 pm
	9 pm

Date: _____   Sobriety Tracker: _____

journal

What makes me sad?

....

....

....

....

....

....

....

....

....

....

....

....

....

personal inventory

'When we retire at night, we constructively review our day'

Was I unkind (cruel, harsh, unfeeling)?

....

Who did I help today?

....

How did I show love to myself? Did I talk negatively to myself?

....

Am I obsessing about anything?

....

What am I proud of today?

....

Was I patient, kind and compassionate? What caused me to lose these attitudes? Do I owe anyone amends?

....

Date: _____   Sobriety Tracker: _____

journal

> What would I tell my younger self if I could?

_____
_____
_____
_____
_____
_____
_____
_____
_____
_____
_____
_____
_____

personal inventory

'When we retire at night, we constructively review our day'

Was I resentful, selfish, dishonest or afraid?
_____

Do I owe an apology?
_____

Have I kept something to myself which should be discussed with another person at once?
_____
_____
_____

Was I kind and loving towards all?
_____

What could I have done better?
_____

Was I thinking about myself most of the time? Or was I thinking of what I could do for others, of what I could pack into the stream of life?
_____
_____
_____

I'm grateful for...

_____
_____
_____

today I accept...

_____
_____

☐ Prayer & meditation   ☐ Service/help someone

☐ Spiritual reading   ☐ Exercise

☐ Call someone   ☐ _____

'On awakening let us think about the twenty-four hours ahead...'

| 6 am |
| 7 am |
| 8 am |
| 9 am |
| 10 am |
| 11 am |
| 12 pm |
| 1 pm |
| 2 pm |
| 3 pm |
| 4 pm |
| 5 pm |
| 6 pm |
| 7 pm |
| 8 pm |
| 9 pm |

'A genuine gratitude for blessings received'

'God, grant me the serenity to accept the things I cannot change'

- ☐ Prayer & meditation
- ☐ Service/help someone
- ☐ Spiritual reading
- ☐ Exercise
- ☐ Call someone
- ☐ ....

'...We consider our plans for the day'

	6 am
	7 am
	8 am
	9 am
	10 am
	11 am
	12 pm
	1 pm
	2 pm
	3 pm
	4 pm
	5 pm
	6 pm
	7 pm
	8 pm
	9 pm

Date:

Sobriety Tracker:

journal

What's my biggest weakness?

personal inventory

'When we retire at night, we constructively review our day'

Did I do something for someone else today?

What did I accomplish today?

What have I done for my recovery today?

Am I taking care of my body?

What could I have done better?

Was I unloving today (cold, unresponsive, indifferent)?

Date: _____   Sobriety Tracker: _____

journal

> What can I do to improve my relationship with my family?

....
....
....
....
....
....
....
....
....
....
....
....

personal inventory

'When we retire at night, we constructively review our day'

Was I resentful, selfish, dishonest or afraid?	....
Do I owe an apology?	....
Have I kept something to myself which should be discussed with another person at once?	....
Was I kind and loving towards all?	....
What could I have done better?	....
Was I thinking about myself most of the time? Or was I thinking of what I could do for others, of what I could pack into the stream of life?	....

I'm grateful for...

....
....
....

today I accept...

....
....

☐ Prayer & meditation ☐ Service/help someone

☐ Spiritual reading ☐ Exercise

☐ Call someone ☐ ....

'On awakening let us think about the twenty-four hours ahead...'

6 am	
7 am	
8 am	
9 am	
10 am	
11 am	
12 pm	
1 pm	
2 pm	
3 pm	
4 pm	
5 pm	
6 pm	
7 pm	
8 pm	
9 pm	

Weekly Check-in

Review of the week

- ☐ Review My vision for the future
- ☐ Review My Rescue Plan
- ☐ Review People to stay in touch with
- ☐ Complete Spiritual Planner

What's been the biggest positive this week?

What fears have been holding me back?

Do I need to ask for some help next week? Is there anyone who needs my help?

Have I been looking after myself this week?

Spiritual Planner

My 2 main spiritual/recovery priorities for this week:

1.

2.

Spiritual and recovery-based activities for the week:

monday

tuesday

wednesday

thursday

friday

saturday

sunday

Date: _____   Sobriety Tracker: _____

journal

What relaxes me?

_____
_____
_____
_____
_____
_____
_____
_____
_____
_____
_____
_____

personal inventory

'When we retire at night, we constructively review our day'

Was I resentful, selfish, dishonest or afraid?
_____
_____

Do I owe an apology?
_____
_____

Have I kept something to myself which should be discussed with another person at once?
_____
_____
_____
_____

Was I kind and loving towards all?
_____
_____

What could I have done better?
_____
_____

Was I thinking about myself most of the time? Or was I thinking of what I could do for others, of what I could pack into the stream of life?
_____
_____
_____

I'm grateful for...

_____
_____
_____

today I accept...

_____
_____

☐ Prayer & meditation   ☐ Service/help someone

☐ Spiritual reading   ☐ Exercise

☐ Call someone   ☐ ....

'On awakening let us think about the twenty-four hours ahead...'

6 am
7 am
8 am
9 am
10 am
11 am
12 pm
1 pm
2 pm
3 pm
4 pm
5 pm
6 pm
7 pm
8 pm
9 pm

'A genuine gratitude for blessings received'

....
....
....
....

'God, grant me the serenity to accept the things I cannot change'

....
....
....
....

- ☐ Prayer & meditation
- ☐ Service/help someone
- ☐ Spiritual reading
- ☐ Exercise
- ☐ Call someone
- ☐ ....

'...We consider our plans for the day'

	6 am
	7 am
	8 am
	9 am
	10 am
	11 am
	12 pm
	1 pm
	2 pm
	3 pm
	4 pm
	5 pm
	6 pm
	7 pm
	8 pm
	9 pm

journal

What makes me angry?

....
....
....
....
....
....
....
....
....
....
....
....
....

personal inventory

'When we retire at night, we constructively review our day'

Was I honest with others and myself today?

What can I celebrate? What could I have done differently?

How was my serenity? Did anything happen that caused me to lose it? What was my part in it?

Am I spending time on myself?

What did I do to connect with my higher power?

Did fear prevent me from doing anything today?

Date: _____   Sobriety Tracker: _____

journal

I create the best results in my life when...

_____
_____
_____
_____
_____
_____
_____
_____
_____
_____
_____
_____
_____
_____
_____

personal inventory

'When we retire at night, we constructively review our day'

Was I resentful, selfish, dishonest or afraid?	_____
Do I owe an apology?	_____
Have I kept something to myself which should be discussed with another person at once?	_____
Was I kind and loving towards all?	_____
What could I have done better?	_____
Was I thinking about myself most of the time? Or was I thinking of what I could do for others, of what I could pack into the stream of life?	_____

I'm grateful for...

....
....
....
....

today I accept...

....
....
....

☐ Prayer & meditation   ☐ Service/help someone

☐ Spiritual reading   ☐ Exercise

☐ Call someone   ☐ ....

'On awakening let us think about the twenty-four hours ahead...'

6 am
7 am
8 am
9 am
10 am
11 am
12 pm
1 pm
2 pm
3 pm
4 pm
5 pm
6 pm
7 pm
8 pm
9 pm

'A genuine gratitude for blessings received'

....
....
....
....

'God, grant me the serenity to accept the things I cannot change'

....
....
....
....

☐ Prayer & meditation   ☐ Service/help someone

☐ Spiritual reading   ☐ Exercise

☐ Call someone   ☐ ....

'...We consider our plans for the day'

6 am

7 am

8 am

9 am

10 am

11 am

12 pm

1 pm

2 pm

3 pm

4 pm

5 pm

6 pm

7 pm

8 pm

9 pm

journal

What is the most important thing in my life?

....
....
....
....
....
....
....
....
....
....
....
....
....
....

personal inventory

'When we retire at night, we constructively review our day'

Have I practiced any of my character defects?

Am I keeping any secrets?

Was I honest? Did I keep my word with everyone? Did I keep my word with myself?

Am I trying to fill the void with external stimuli?

Did I learn something useful today? Or was I a mental loafer?

Was I concerned today with thoughts or behaviours linked to my addiction?

Date: _____ Sobriety Tracker: _____

journal

Is there anyone I need to forgive?

_____
_____
_____
_____
_____
_____
_____
_____
_____
_____
_____
_____
_____

personal inventory

'When we retire at night, we constructively review our day'

Was I resentful, selfish, dishonest or afraid?
_____
_____

Do I owe an apology?
_____
_____

Have I kept something to myself which should be discussed with another person at once?
_____
_____

Was I kind and loving towards all?
_____
_____

What could I have done better?
_____
_____

Was I thinking about myself most of the time? Or was I thinking of what I could do for others, of what I could pack into the stream of life?
_____
_____

I'm grateful for...

_____
_____
_____
_____

today I accept...

_____
_____

☐ Prayer & meditation   ☐ Service/help someone

☐ Spiritual reading   ☐ Exercise

☐ Call someone   ☐ ....

'On awakening let us think about the twenty-four hours ahead...'

6 am
7 am
8 am
9 am
10 am
11 am
12 pm
1 pm
2 pm
3 pm
4 pm
5 pm
6 pm
7 pm
8 pm
9 pm

'A genuine gratitude for blessings received'

'God, grant me the serenity to accept the things I cannot change'

- ☐ Prayer & meditation
- ☐ Service/help someone
- ☐ Spiritual reading
- ☐ Exercise
- ☐ Call someone
- ☐ ....

'...We consider our plans for the day'

6 am

7 am

8 am

9 am

10 am

11 am

12 pm

1 pm

2 pm

3 pm

4 pm

5 pm

6 pm

7 pm

8 pm

9 pm

journal

Am I generally positive or negative?

personal inventory

'When we retire at night, we constructively review our day'

How did I take care of my health (physical, emotional, spiritual) today?

What have I enjoyed about today?

How did I show love to others? Did I act unlovingly towards anyone?

Who neds my prayers today?

Am I holding any resentments?

How is my spiritual condition?

Date: _____ Sobriety Tracker: _____

journal

What or who inspires me?

_____
_____
_____
_____
_____
_____
_____
_____
_____
_____
_____
_____
_____

personal inventory

'When we retire at night, we constructively review our day'

Was I resentful, selfish, dishonest or afraid?	
Do I owe an apology?	
Have I kept something to myself which should be discussed with another person at once?	
Was I kind and loving towards all?	
What could I have done better?	
Was I thinking about myself most of the time? Or was I thinking of what I could do for others, of what I could pack into the stream of life?	

I'm grateful for...

_____
_____
_____
_____

today I accept...

_____
_____
_____

☐ Prayer & meditation   ☐ Service/help someone

☐ Spiritual reading   ☐ Exercise

☐ Call someone   ☐ _____

'On awakening let us think about the twenty-four hours ahead...'

6 am
7 am
8 am
9 am
10 am
11 am
12 pm
1 pm
2 pm
3 pm
4 pm
5 pm
6 pm
7 pm
8 pm
9 pm

Weekly Check-in

Review of the week

- ☐ Review How I'll know if I'm heading for a relapse
- ☐ Review My Character Defects
- ☐ Review People to stay in touch with
- ☐ Complete Spiritual Planner

What's gone well this week?

What are the biggest distractions in my life? How can I remove them?

Which part of the program do I need to prioritise next week?

How is my spiritual condition?

Spiritual Planner

My 2 main spiritual/recovery priorities for this week:

1.

2.

Spiritual and recovery-based activities for the week:

monday

tuesday

wednesday

thursday

friday

saturday

sunday

Date: _____ Sobriety Tracker: _____

journal

> Do I need to forgive myself for anything?

....
....
....
....
....
....
....
....
....
....
....
....
....

personal inventory

'When we retire at night, we constructively review our day'

Was I resentful, selfish, dishonest or afraid?	....
Do I owe an apology?	....
Have I kept something to myself which should be discussed with another person at once?	....
Was I kind and loving towards all?	....
What could I have done better?	....
Was I thinking about myself most of the time? Or was I thinking of what I could do for others, of what I could pack into the stream of life?	....

I'm grateful for...

....
....
....

today I accept...

....
....

☐ Prayer & meditation   ☐ Service/help someone

☐ Spiritual reading   ☐ Exercise

☐ Call someone   ☐ ....

'On awakening let us think about the twenty-four hours ahead...'

6 am
7 am
8 am
9 am
10 am
11 am
12 pm
1 pm
2 pm
3 pm
4 pm
5 pm
6 pm
7 pm
8 pm
9 pm

'A genuine gratitude for blessings received'

'God, grant me the serenity to accept the things I cannot change'

- ☐ Prayer & meditation
- ☐ Service/help someone
- ☐ Spiritual reading
- ☐ Exercise
- ☐ Call someone
- ☐ ....

'...We consider our plans for the day'

	6 am
	7 am
	8 am
	9 am
	10 am
	11 am
	12 pm
	1 pm
	2 pm
	3 pm
	4 pm
	5 pm
	6 pm
	7 pm
	8 pm
	9 pm

journal

Is there anything missing in my life?

personal inventory

'When we retire at night, we constructively review our day'

Was I unkind (cruel, harsh, unfeeling)?

Who did I help today?

How did I show love to myself? Did I talk negatively to myself?

Am I obsessing about anything?

What am I proud of today?

Was I patient, kind and compassionate? What caused me to lose these attitudes? Do I owe anyone amends?

Date: _____   Sobriety Tracker: _____

journal

What am I good at?
What am I bad at?

_____
_____
_____
_____
_____
_____
_____
_____
_____
_____
_____
_____
_____
_____

personal inventory

'When we retire at night, we constructively review our day'

Was I resentful, selfish, dishonest or afraid?	
Do I owe an apology?	
Have I kept something to myself which should be discussed with another person at once?	
Was I kind and loving towards all?	
What could I have done better?	
Was I thinking about myself most of the time? Or was I thinking of what I could do for others, of what I could pack into the stream of life?	

I'm grateful for...

_____
_____
_____
_____

today I accept...

_____
_____
_____

☐ Prayer & meditation   ☐ Service/help someone

☐ Spiritual reading   ☐ Exercise

☐ Call someone   ☐ ....

'On awakening let us think about the twenty-four hours ahead...'

6 am	
7 am	
8 am	
9 am	
10 am	
11 am	
12 pm	
1 pm	
2 pm	
3 pm	
4 pm	
5 pm	
6 pm	
7 pm	
8 pm	
9 pm	

'A genuine gratitude for blessings received'

....
....
....
....

'God, grant me the serenity to accept the things I cannot change'

....
....
....
....

☐ Prayer & meditation   ☐ Service/help someone

☐ Spiritual reading   ☐ Exercise

☐ Call someone   ☐ ....

'...We consider our plans for the day'

	6 am
	7 am
	8 am
	9 am
	10 am
	11 am
	12 pm
	1 pm
	2 pm
	3 pm
	4 pm
	5 pm
	6 pm
	7 pm
	8 pm
	9 pm

Date: _____   Sobriety Tracker: _____

journal

What's my happiest memory from my childhood?

....
....
....
....
....
....
....
....
....
....
....
....

personal inventory

'When we retire at night, we constructively review our day'

Did I do something for someone else today?

What did I accomplish today?

What have I done for my recovery today?

Am I taking care of my body?

What could I have done better?

Was I unloving today (cold, unresponsive, indifferent)?

Date: _____   Sobriety Tracker: _____

journal

How often do I ask other for help?

_____
_____
_____
_____
_____
_____
_____
_____
_____
_____
_____
_____

personal inventory

'When we retire at night, we constructively review our day'

Was I resentful, selfish, dishonest or afraid?
_____
_____

Do I owe an apology?
_____
_____

Have I kept something to myself which should be discussed with another person at once?
_____
_____
_____
_____

Was I kind and loving towards all?
_____
_____

What could I have done better?
_____
_____

Was I thinking about myself most of the time? Or was I thinking of what I could do for others, of what I could pack into the stream of life?
_____
_____
_____
_____
_____

I'm grateful for...
_____
_____
_____
_____

today I accept...
_____
_____
_____

- ☐ Prayer & meditation
- ☐ Service/help someone
- ☐ Spiritual reading
- ☐ Exercise
- ☐ Call someone
- ☐ ....

'On awakening let us think about the twenty-four hours ahead...'

6 am	
7 am	
8 am	
9 am	
10 am	
11 am	
12 pm	
1 pm	
2 pm	
3 pm	
4 pm	
5 pm	
6 pm	
7 pm	
8 pm	
9 pm	

'A genuine gratitude for blessings received'

_____
_____
_____
_____

'God, grant me the serenity to accept the things I cannot change'

_____
_____
_____

☐ Prayer & meditation   ☐ Service/help someone

☐ Spiritual reading   ☐ Exercise

☐ Call someone   ☐ ....

'...We consider our plans for the day'

	6 am
	7 am
	8 am
	9 am
	10 am
	11 am
	12 pm
	1 pm
	2 pm
	3 pm
	4 pm
	5 pm
	6 pm
	7 pm
	8 pm
	9 pm

Date: _____   Sobriety Tracker: _____

journal

> What does my ego get in the way of?

_____
_____
_____
_____
_____
_____
_____
_____
_____
_____
_____
_____
_____
_____
_____
_____

personal inventory

'When we retire at night, we constructively review our day'

Was I honest with others and myself today?

What can I celebrate? What could I have done differently?

How was my serenity? Did anything happen that caused me to lose it? What was my part in it?

Am I spending time on myself?

What did I do to connect with my higher power?

Did fear prevent me from doing anything today?

Date: _____   Sobriety Tracker: _____

journal

> Where can I give more of my time, money or support?

....
....
....
....
....
....
....
....
....
....
....
....
....
....
....

personal inventory

'When we retire at night, we constructively review our day'

Was I resentful, selfish, dishonest or afraid?
....

Do I owe an apology?
....

Have I kept something to myself which should be discussed with another person at once?
....
....
....

Was I kind and loving towards all?
....

What could I have done better?
....

Was I thinking about myself most of the time? Or was I thinking of what I could do for others, of what I could pack into the stream of life?
....
....
....
....

I'm grateful for...

....
....
....
....

today I accept...

....
....

☐ Prayer & meditation ☐ Service/help someone

☐ Spiritual reading ☐ Exercise

☐ Call someone ☐ ....

'On awakening let us think about the twenty-four hours ahead...'

6 am
7 am
8 am
9 am
10 am
11 am
12 pm
1 pm
2 pm
3 pm
4 pm
5 pm
6 pm
7 pm
8 pm
9 pm

Weekly Check-in

Review of the week

- [ ] Review My Rock Bottom
- [ ] Review My Character Defects
- [ ] Review People to stay in touch with
- [ ] Complete Spiritual Planner

What have I achieved this week?

What's not working? What am I willing to do about it?

What one thing can I do next week that will have the biggest positive impact on my life?

What do I need to make a decision about?

Spiritual Planner

My 2 main spiritual/recovery priorities for this week:

1.

2.

Spiritual and recovery-based activities for the week:

monday

tuesday

wednesday

thursday

friday

saturday

sunday

I came, at my first surrender, not only into consciousness of God but into usefulness for God and others. I was able to do, through God's help, what no one has ever been able or ever will be able to do alone, which is to supplement the all-important "why" of life with the still more important "how" of living. I was able to begin solving my own problems and, for the first time in my experience, was given the power to begin helping others. I no longer wished well to "myself alone". Dear God, I pray to surrender again today.

Consciousness of God

Bill P. and Lisa D. *The 12 Step Prayer Book. 2nd ed.* Center City, Minn.: Hazelden, 2004

Six-monthly Review

Six-Monthly Review

Congratulations for having made it this far. Our hope is that this journal has helped you consistently prioritise your recovery, and use the spiritual toolkit available to you every day. Hopefully you've learnt a lot about yourself, your relationships and your recovery.

Let's take a little time now, and reflect on your journey over the last six months or so. It's a time of celebration, as it's taken great commitment and dedication to get here. The following questions will help highlight areas of significance, and get you into a great place to look ahead at the upcoming six months.

We would truly love to hear from you. Write to us at recovery@12stepjournals.com and tell us about your experiences since starting the journal, your breakthroughs, your thoughts on this book and any suggestions for improvement. We will personally and gratefully read every email, and where possible aim to respond to all.

If this journal has been helpful to you, help us to reach others who may also benefit, by leaving a review. And don't forget to re-order your *12 Step Journal* for the six months ahead.

What's been the biggest success of the last six months?

What else do I have to celebrate?

How am I going to celebrate these achievements?

What's been the biggest lesson I've learned since starting this journal?

What have I learned about myself? (Have a look through the 'Reflections' section)

How is my life now, compared to six months ago?

What has made the biggest positive impact on my life over the last six months?

What's gotten in the way of my sobriety and/or serenity?

Looking at the 'My Vision for the Future' worksheet, have I moved towards or away from that vision?

What are some words that I'd use to describe the last six months?

Which words would I choose to describe how I want the six months ahead to be?

What commitments do I want to carry forward to the six months ahead?

Dear God,

I had another anniversary today, one more year in recovery.

It has been difficult at times, but it has allowed many

blessings. I am a human being again. I feel new strength

in my body, spirit and mind. The world has never looked so

good. I have the respect of my friends and family. I am

productive in my work. I do not miss the slippery people

and places. When I have been tempted, You, my Higher

Power, have sustained me. I have found a home in the

Fellowship and friends support me. Stay close by me, God.

I thank You. This is the life I love.

Anniversary Prayer

Bill P. and Lisa D. *The 12 Step Prayer Book. 2nd ed.* Center City, Minn.: Hazelden, 2004

References

"On awakening let us think about the twenty-four hours ahead. We consider our plans for the day"

Alcoholics Anonymous. (2001). *Alcoholics Anonymous, 4th Edition.* New York: A.A. World Services. p.86

(AKA 'The Big Book of AA')

journal

Date: Sobriety Tracker:

When did I last make a new friend?

I'm grateful for…

today I accept…

Prayer & meditation   Service/help someone

Spiritual reading   Exercise

Call someone

'On awakening let us think about the twenty-four hours ahead…'

6 am
7 am
8 am
9 am
10 am
11 am
12 pm
1 pm
2 pm
3 pm
4 pm
5 pm
6 pm
7 pm
8 pm
9 pm

personal inventory   *'When we retire at night, we constructively review our day'*

Was I resentful, selfish, dishonest or afraid?

Do I owe an apology?

Have I kept something to myself which should be discussed with another person at once?

Was I kind and loving towards all?

What could I have done better?

Was I thinking about myself most of the time? Or was I thinking of what I could do for others, of what I could pack into the stream of life?

"Was I resentful, selfish, dishonest or afraid?"

"Do I owe an apology?"

"Have I kept something to myself which should be discussed with another person at once?"

"Was I kind and loving towards all?"

"What could I have done better?"

"Was I thinking about myself most of the time? Or was I thinking of what I could do for others, of what I could pack into the stream of life?"

Alcoholics Anonymous. (2001). *Alcoholics Anonymous, 4th Edition*. New York: A.A. World Services. p.86

(AKA 'The Big Book of AA')

"A genuine gratitude for blessings received"

Alcoholics Anonymous. (1995). *Twelve Steps and Twelve Traditions*. New York: Alcoholics Anonymous World Services. p.95

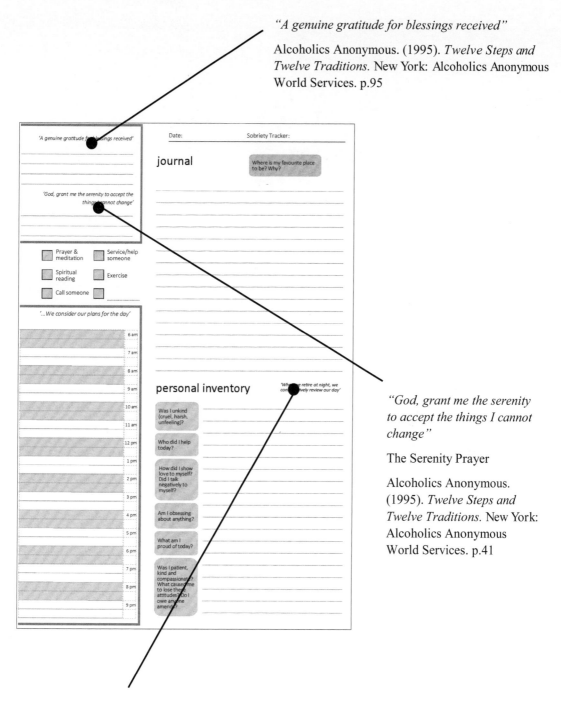

"God, grant me the serenity to accept the things I cannot change"

The Serenity Prayer

Alcoholics Anonymous. (1995). *Twelve Steps and Twelve Traditions*. New York: Alcoholics Anonymous World Services. p.41

"When we retire at night, we constructively review our day"

Alcoholics Anonymous. (2001). *Alcoholics Anonymous, 4th Edition*. New York: A.A. World Services. p.86

(AKA 'The Big Book of AA')